HOCKEY LIFE LOG BOOK

A COMIC STYLE BOOK TO CAPTURE GAME HIGHLIGHTS!

Please note I am creating similar books for other sports like Baseball, Soccer, etc. As well, most books can also be found in an Exhibition and Tournament Edition.

Introduction

Healthy competition can be linked to many great things like greater empathy, more confidence and social skills. Not to mention stylishly handling wins and losses! With so many benefits, it's clear that developing the right type of mindset early on can help kids become better athletes and better humans.

There are many effective ways to create a healthy, competitive mindset and to keep trying regardless of the final score. Reviewing a game right after the event is a great start. Winning is powerful but so is losing if you can learn from this event. What created success? Was it individual effort? Teamwork? What skills were displayed? What could have been done better?

Taking notes after a game is ideal. But what if you just don't feel like the creative type or you're motivationally challenged? Then this Log Book is for you!

Enjoy the first few pages of the Log book highlighting you and your team at the beginning of the season. What's your team name, colors, jersey, coach? If you could design your equipment, what would it look like? ..... and more.

Then start to highlight each game through prompted questions relating to each game set out in comic book form with extra areas to make notes.
At the end of the book, you have a few summary pages to fill out about the season as a whole and you can make notes for the nest season. Additionally, you'll have a notebook of great memories!

Good Luck!

This Log Book is designed to develop your ability to look back and recognize what needs to be worked on. It's a way to narrow your attention and connect hard work and discipline towards what makes a successful game. Using prompts is an easy way to review the game and help set up the next game day with purpose.

Remember by reviewing play and setting goals, athletes can write their own path to peak performance.

NAME:

MY TEAM:

MY POSITION:

MY NUMBER:

COACH:

ASST COACH(S):

DESIGN YOUR JERSEY

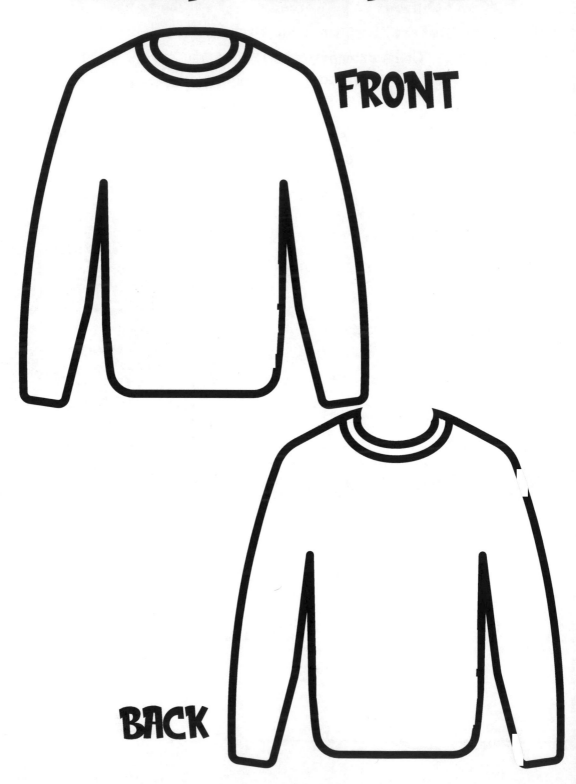

FRONT

BACK

DESIGN YOUR HELMET

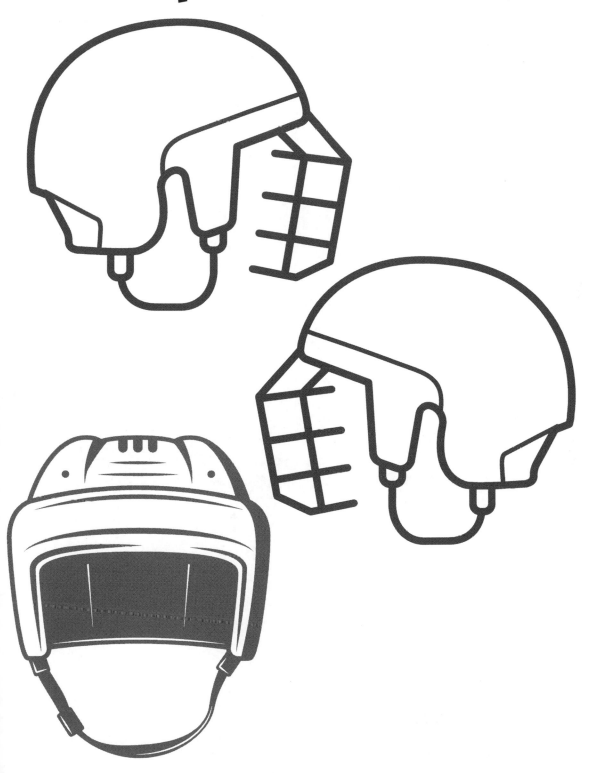

DESIGN YOUR STICK

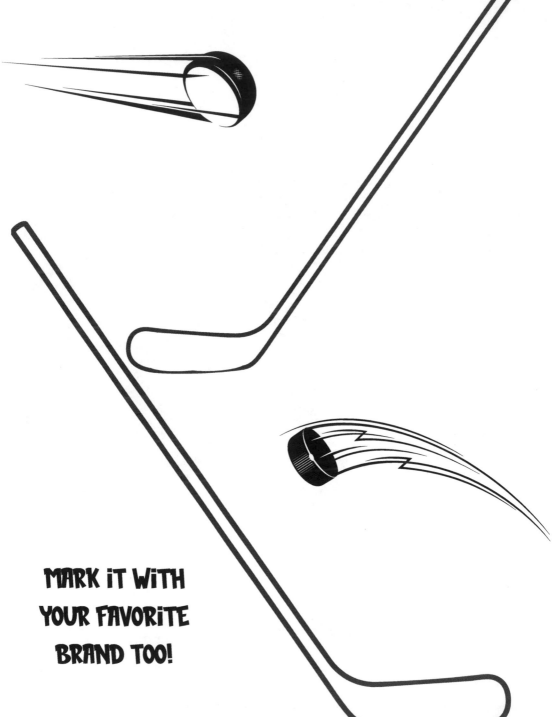

MARK IT WITH YOUR FAVORITE BRAND TOO!

HOW LONG HAVE YOU BEEN PLAYING?

HOW OLD ARE YOU NOW?

WHAT DO YOU THINK OF YOUR COACH AND ASST COACH?

I WILL PLAY BY THE RULES

MY LONG TERM GOALS FOR THIS SPORT?

-
-
-
-

NOTES

PRE-GAME EQUIPMENT CHECKLIST

SKATES .... ☐

JERSEY .... ☐

HELMET .... ☐

SHORTS .... ☐

SOCKS .... ☐

STICK .... ☐

TAPE .... ☐

JOCK/JILL .... ☐

SHOULDER PADS/CHEST PROTECTOR .... ☐

SHIN PADS .... ☐

NECK GUARD .... ☐

ELBOW PADS .... ☐

MOUTH GUARD .... ☐

GLOVES .... ☐

WATER BOTTLES .... ☐

OTHER NOTES

GAME DAY

DATE:

LOCATION:

START TIME: **END TIME:**

OPPONENT TEAM:

FROM:

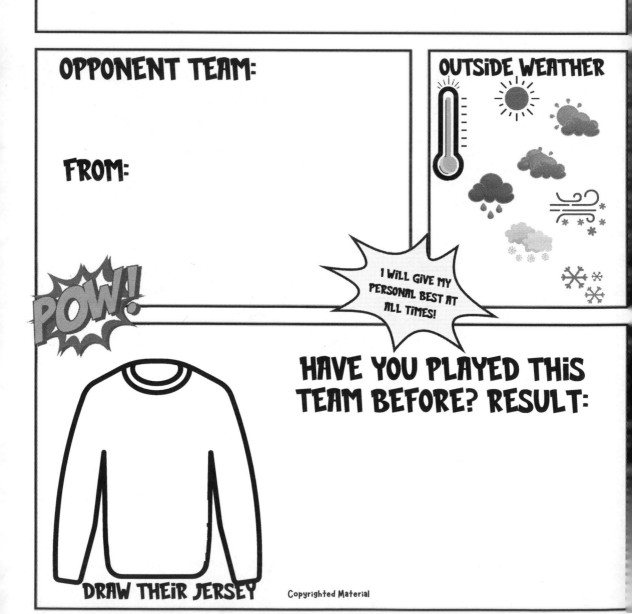

OUTSIDE WEATHER

I WILL GIVE MY PERSONAL BEST AT ALL TIMES!

POW!!

HAVE YOU PLAYED THIS TEAM BEFORE? RESULT:

DRAW THEIR JERSEY

FINAL SCORE

WIN!   OUCH!   YEAH!!   LOSS

THEM   US

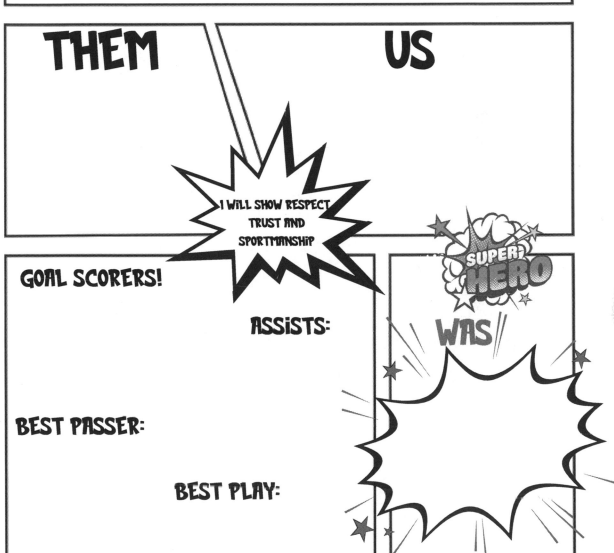

I WILL SHOW RESPECT TRUST AND SPORTMANSHIP

GOAL SCORERS!

ASSISTS:

SUPER HERO WAS

BEST PASSER:

BEST PLAY:

CIRCLE THE EMOJIS THAT BEST REPRESENT YOUR FEELINGS AFTER THE GAME

OR DRAW YOUR OWN!

SKILLS USED

DID YOU PLAY A GAME SONG? WHAT WAS IT?

COACHES WORDS AFTER GAME

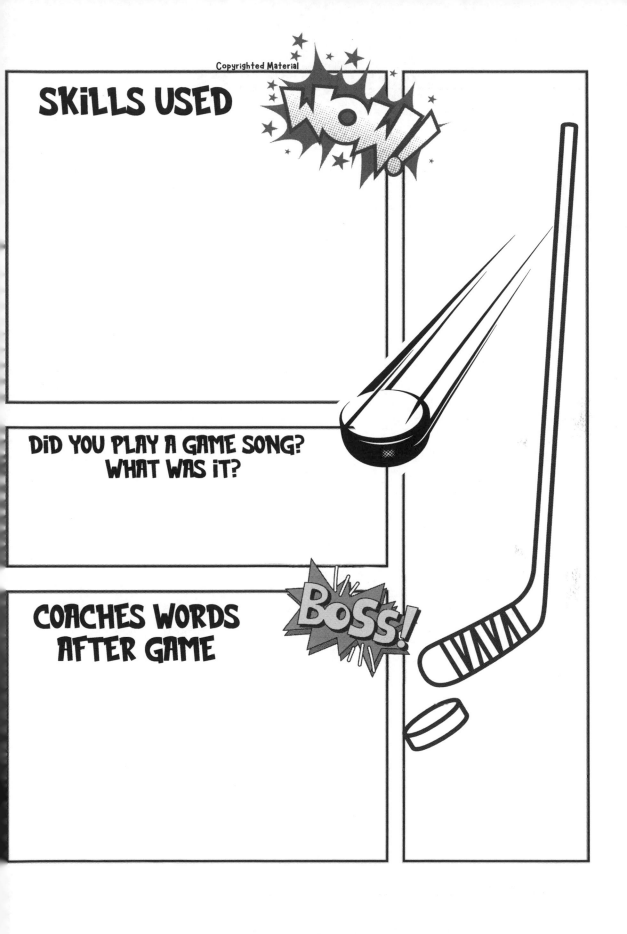

THINGS TO IMPROVE

FIGHTS?

KAPOW!!

WHAAA?!

PENALTY MINUTES

BAD CALLS

ENHANCE THESE SKILLS

DID YOU RESPECT YOUR TEAMMATES?

DID YOU PASS EFFECTIVELY?

DID YOU CHEER FOR YOUR TEAM?

DID YOU RESPECT YOUR OPPONENTS?

CHEER, NOT JEER!

DID YOU PLAY BY THE RULES?

CONNECT WINNING WITH EFFORT!

DID YOU SHAKE HANDS?

OTHER NOTES

IT'S EASY TO THINK OF WINNING AS THE RESULT OF TALENT OR LUCK. REMEMBER THAT POSITIVE OUTCOMES ARE THE RESULT OF LOTS OF EFFORT. USUALLY THE BEST PLAYERS PRACTICE THE MOST AND WORK THE HARDEST!!

GAME DAY

DATE:

LOCATION:

START TIME: END TIME:

OPPONENT TEAM:

FROM:

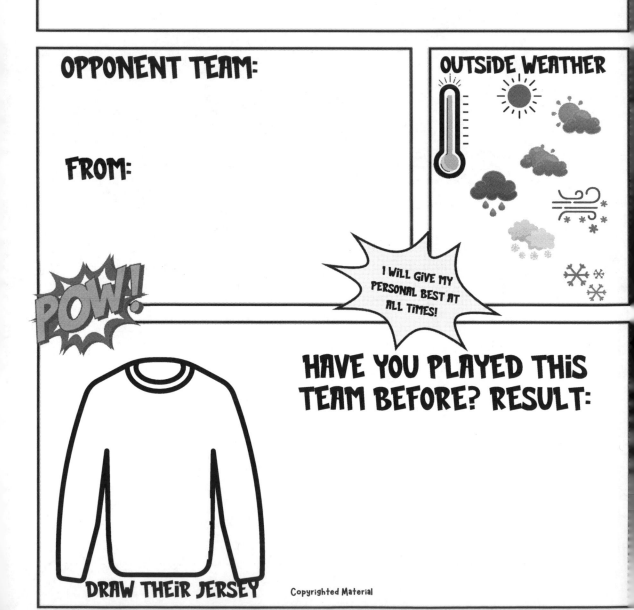

OUTSIDE WEATHER

I WILL GIVE MY PERSONAL BEST AT ALL TIMES!

POW!

HAVE YOU PLAYED THIS TEAM BEFORE? RESULT:

DRAW THEIR JERSEY

FINAL SCORE

   LOSS

THEM

US

I WILL SHOW RESPECT TRUST AND SPORTMANSHIP

GOAL SCORERS!

ASSISTS:

WAS

BEST PASSER:

BEST PLAY:

CIRCLE THE EMOJIS THAT BEST REPRESENT YOUR FEELINGS AFTER THE GAME

&?#!*

OR DRAW YOUR OWN!

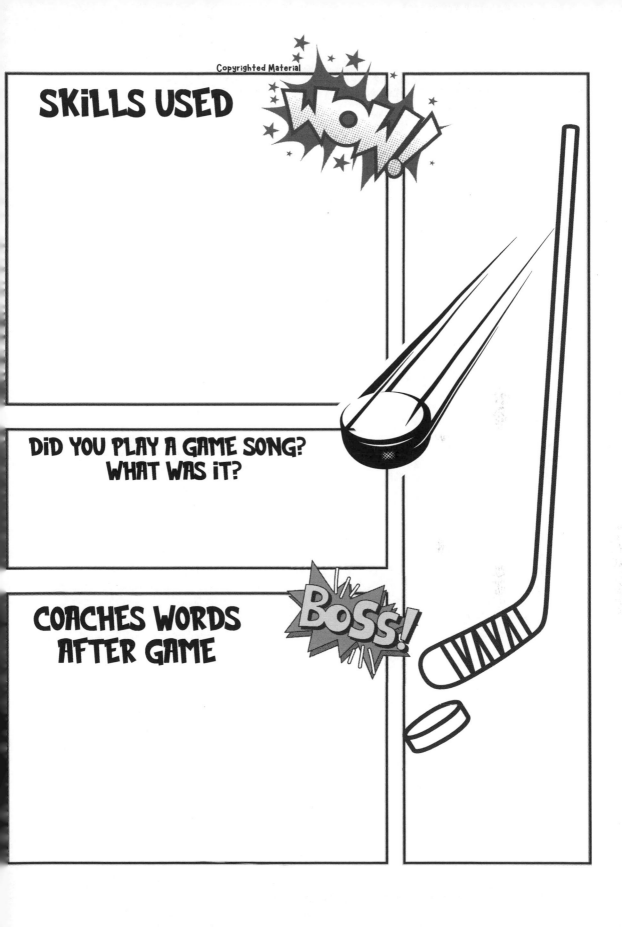

SKILLS USED

DID YOU PLAY A GAME SONG?
WHAT WAS IT?

COACHES WORDS
AFTER GAME

THINGS TO IMPROVE

WHAAAA?!

FIGHTS?

KAPOW!

PENALTY MINUTES

BAD CALLS

ENHANCE THESE SKILLS

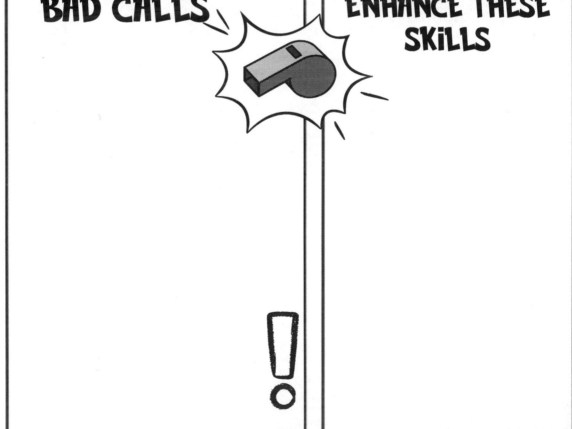

DiD YOU RESPECT YOUR TEAMMATES?

DiD YOU PASS EFFECTIVELY?

DiD YOU CHEER FOR YOUR TEAM?

DiD YOU RESPECT YOUR OPPONENTS?

CHEER, NOT JEER!

DiD YOU PLAY BY THE RULES?

CONNECT WINNING WITH EFFORT!

DiD YOU SHAKE HANDS?

OTHER NOTES

IT'S EASY TO THINK OF WINNING AS THE RESULT OF TALENT OR LUCK. REMEMBER THAT POSITIVE OUTCOMES ARE THE RESULT OF LOTS OF EFFORT. USUALLY THE BEST PLAYERS PRACTICE THE MOST AND WORK THE HARDEST!!

GAME DAY

DATE:

LOCATION:

START TIME: **END TIME:**

OPPONENT TEAM:

FROM:

OUTSIDE WEATHER

I WILL GIVE MY PERSONAL BEST AT ALL TIMES!

POW!!

HAVE YOU PLAYED THIS TEAM BEFORE? RESULT:

DRAW THEIR JERSEY

FINAL SCORE

WIN!   OUCH!   YEAH!!   LOSS

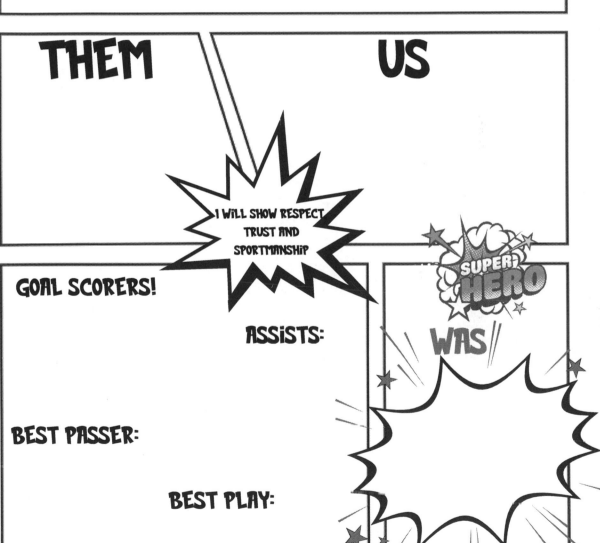

THEM   US

I WILL SHOW RESPECT TRUST AND SPORTMANSHIP

SUPER HERO WAS

GOAL SCORERS!

ASSISTS:

BEST PASSER:

BEST PLAY:

CIRCLE THE EMOJIS THAT BEST REPRESENT YOUR FEELINGS AFTER THE GAME

OR DRAW YOUR OWN!

SKILLS USED

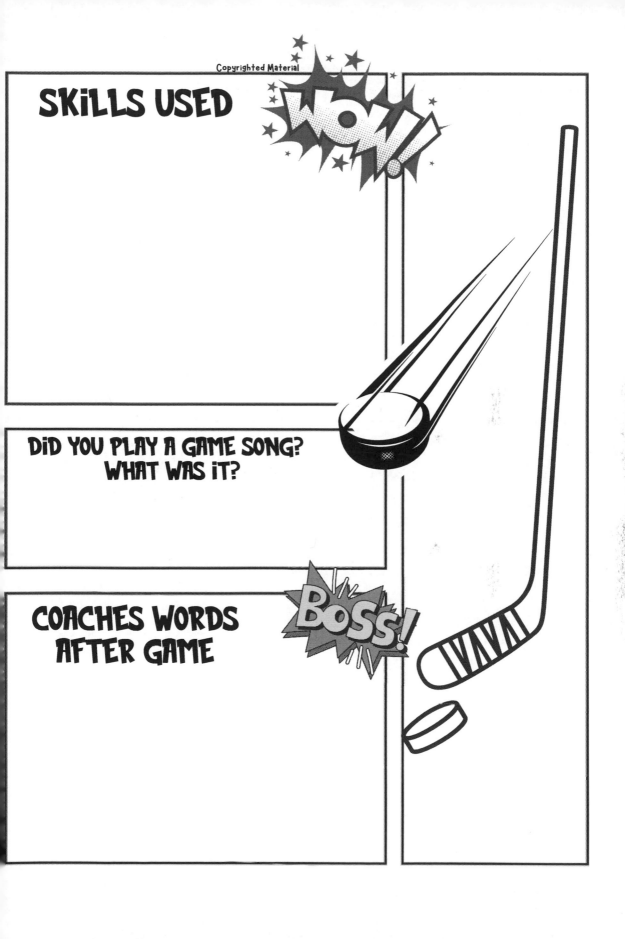

DID YOU PLAY A GAME SONG? WHAT WAS IT?

COACHES WORDS AFTER GAME

THINGS TO IMPROVE

WHAAAA?!

FIGHTS?

KAPOW!

PENALTY MINUTES

BAD CALLS

ENHANCE THESE SKILLS

OTHER NOTES

IT'S EASY TO THINK OF WINNING AS THE RESULT OF TALENT OR LUCK. REMEMBER THAT POSITIVE OUTCOMES ARE THE RESULT OF LOTS OF EFFORT. USUALLY THE BEST PLAYERS PRACTICE THE MOST AND WORK THE HARDEST!!

GAME DAY

DATE:

LOCATION:

START TIME: **END TIME:**

OPPONENT TEAM:

FROM:

OUTSIDE WEATHER

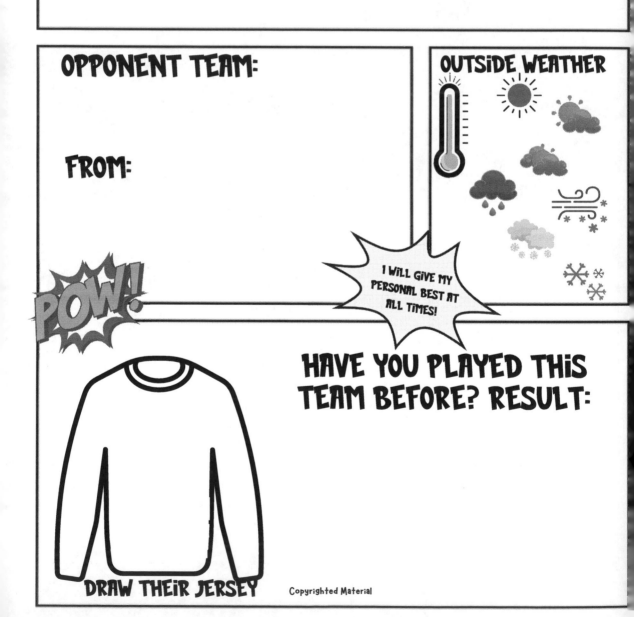

I WILL GIVE MY PERSONAL BEST AT ALL TIMES!

POW!

HAVE YOU PLAYED THIS TEAM BEFORE? RESULT:

DRAW THEIR JERSEY

FINAL SCORE

WIN! OUCH! YEAH!! LOSS

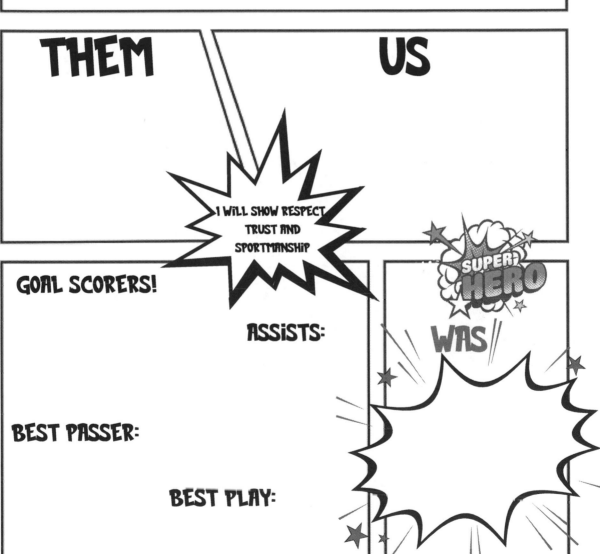

THEM

US

I WILL SHOW RESPECT TRUST AND SPORTMANSHIP

GOAL SCORERS!

ASSISTS:

SUPER HERO WAS

BEST PASSER:

BEST PLAY:

CIRCLE THE EMOJIS THAT BEST REPRESENT YOUR FEELINGS AFTER THE GAME

OR DRAW YOUR OWN!

SKILLS USED

DID YOU PLAY A GAME SONG? WHAT WAS IT?

COACHES WORDS AFTER GAME

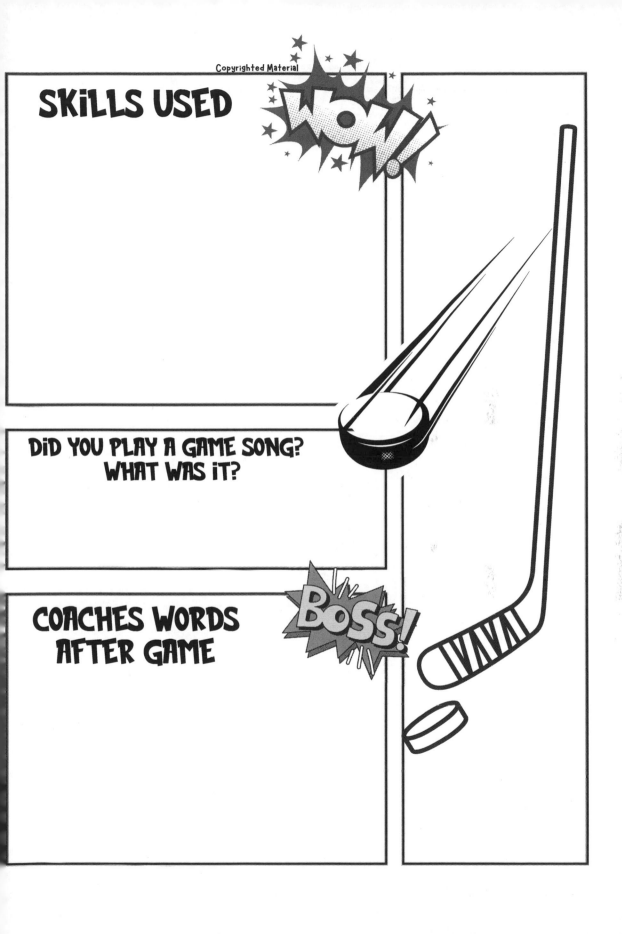

THINGS TO IMPROVE

WHAAA?!

FIGHTS?

KAPOW!

PENALTY MINUTES

BAD CALLS

ENHANCE THESE SKILLS

DiD YOU RESPECT YOUR TEAMMATES?

DID YOU PASS EFFECTIVELY?

DID YOU CHEER FOR YOUR TEAM?

DiD YOU RESPECT YOUR OPPONENTS?

CHEER, NOT JEER!

DID YOU PLAY BY THE RULES?

CONNECT WINNING WITH EFFORT!

DID YOU SHAKE HANDS?

OTHER NOTES

IT'S EASY TO THINK OF WINNING AS THE RESULT OF TALENT OR LUCK. REMEMBER THAT POSITIVE OUTCOMES ARE THE RESULT OF LOTS OF EFFORT. USUALLY THE BEST PLAYERS PRACTICE THE MOST AND WORK THE HARDEST!!

GAME DAY

DATE:

LOCATION:

START TIME: **END TIME:**

OPPONENT TEAM:

FROM:

OUTSIDE WEATHER

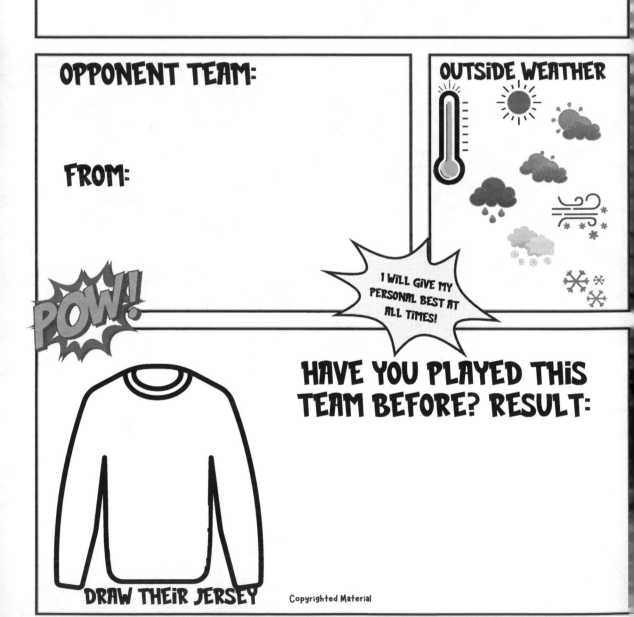

I WILL GIVE MY PERSONAL BEST AT ALL TIMES!

POW!!

HAVE YOU PLAYED THIS TEAM BEFORE? RESULT:

DRAW THEIR JERSEY

FINAL SCORE

THEM

US

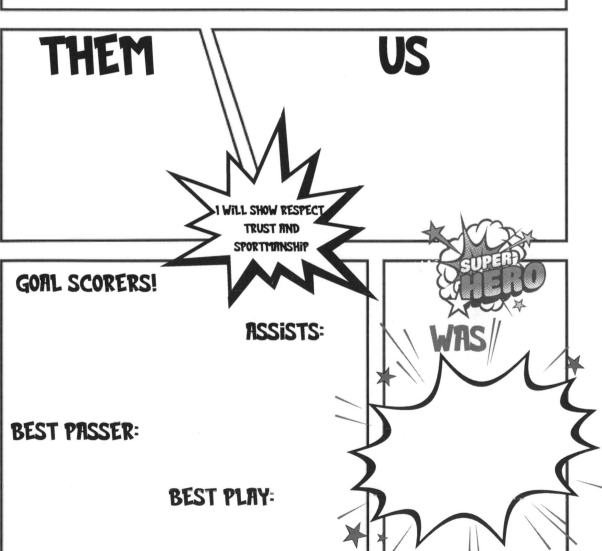

I WILL SHOW RESPECT TRUST AND SPORTMANSHIP

GOAL SCORERS!

ASSISTS:

SUPER HERO

WAS

BEST PASSER:

BEST PLAY:

CIRCLE THE EMOJIS THAT BEST REPRESENT YOUR FEELINGS AFTER THE GAME

OR DRAW YOUR OWN!

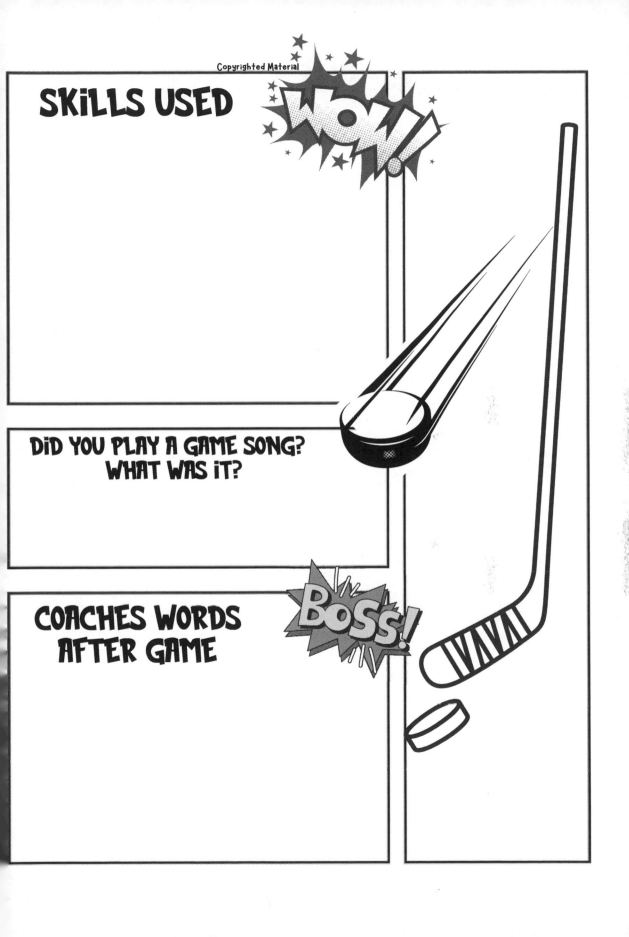

SKILLS USED

DID YOU PLAY A GAME SONG? WHAT WAS IT?

COACHES WORDS AFTER GAME

THINGS TO IMPROVE

WHAAAA?!

FiGHTS?

KAPOW!

PENALTY MiNUTES

BAD CALLS

ENHANCE THESE SKiLLS

DID YOU RESPECT YOUR TEAMMATES?

DID YOU PASS EFFECTIVELY?

DID YOU CHEER FOR YOUR TEAM?

DID YOU RESPECT YOUR OPPONENTS?

CHEER, NOT JEER!

DID YOU PLAY BY THE RULES?

CONNECT WINNING WITH EFFORT!

DID YOU SHAKE HANDS?

OTHER NOTES

IT'S EASY TO THINK OF WINNING AS THE RESULT OF TALENT OR LUCK. REMEMBER THAT POSITIVE OUTCOMES ARE THE RESULT OF LOTS OF EFFORT. USUALLY THE BEST PLAYERS PRACTICE THE MOST AND WORK THE HARDEST!!

GAME DAY

DATE:

LOCATION:

START TIME: END TIME:

OPPONENT TEAM:

FROM:

OUTSIDE WEATHER

I WILL GIVE MY PERSONAL BEST AT ALL TIMES!

POW!!

HAVE YOU PLAYED THIS TEAM BEFORE? RESULT:

DRAW THEIR JERSEY

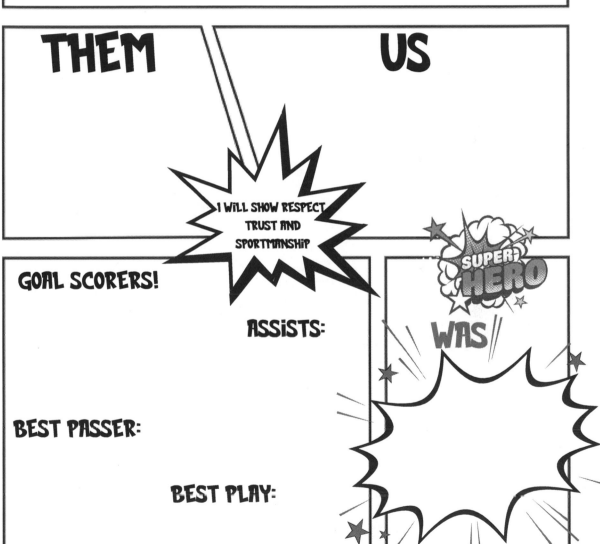

CIRCLE THE EMOJIS THAT BEST REPRESENT YOUR FEELINGS AFTER THE GAME

OR DRAW YOUR OWN!

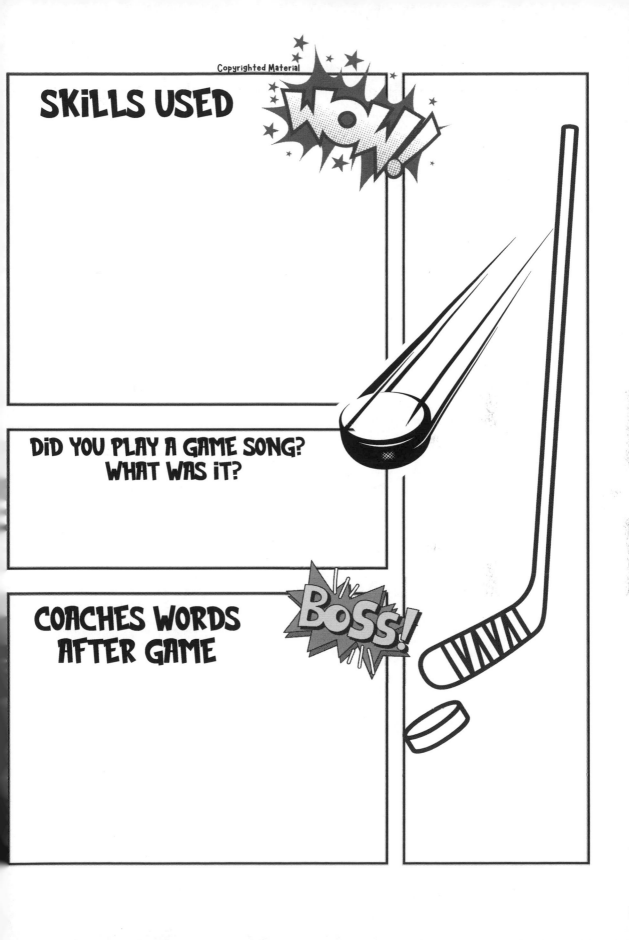

SKILLS USED

DiD YOU PLAY A GAME SONG? WHAT WAS iT?

COACHES WORDS AFTER GAME

THINGS TO IMPROVE

WHAAA?!

FIGHTS?

KAPOW!!

PENALTY MINUTES

BAD CALLS

ENHANCE THESE SKILLS

DID YOU RESPECT YOUR TEAMMATES?

DID YOU PASS EFFECTIVELY?

DID YOU CHEER FOR YOUR TEAM?

DID YOU RESPECT YOUR OPPONENTS?

CHEER, NOT JEER!

DID YOU PLAY BY THE RULES?

CONNECT WINNING WITH EFFORT!

DID YOU SHAKE HANDS?

OTHER NOTES

IT'S EASY TO THINK OF WINNING AS THE RESULT OF TALENT OR LUCK. REMEMBER THAT POSITIVE OUTCOMES ARE THE RESULT OF LOTS OF EFFORT. USUALLY THE BEST PLAYERS PRACTICE THE MOST AND WORK THE HARDEST!!

GAME DAY

DATE:

LOCATION:

START TIME: END TIME:

OPPONENT TEAM:

FROM:

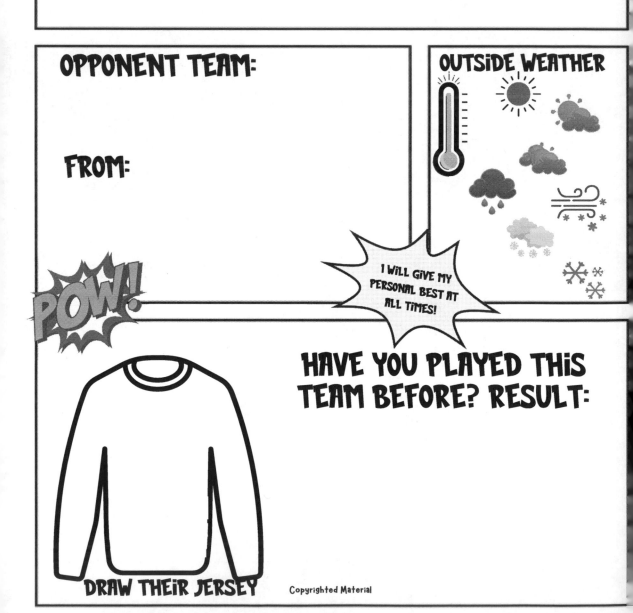

OUTSIDE WEATHER

I WILL GIVE MY PERSONAL BEST AT ALL TIMES!

POW!!

HAVE YOU PLAYED THIS TEAM BEFORE? RESULT:

DRAW THEIR JERSEY

FINAL SCORE

THEM

US

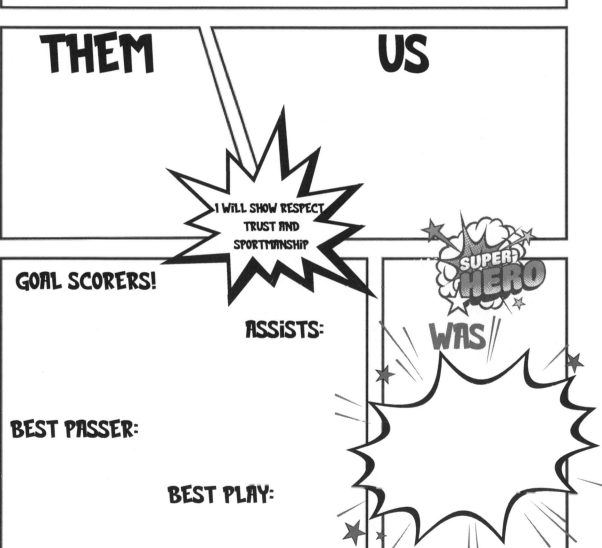

I WILL SHOW RESPECT TRUST AND SPORTMANSHIP

GOAL SCORERS!

ASSISTS:

BEST PASSER:

BEST PLAY:

SUPER HERO WAS

CIRCLE THE EMOJIS THAT BEST REPRESENT YOUR FEELINGS AFTER THE GAME

OR DRAW YOUR OWN!

SKILLS USED

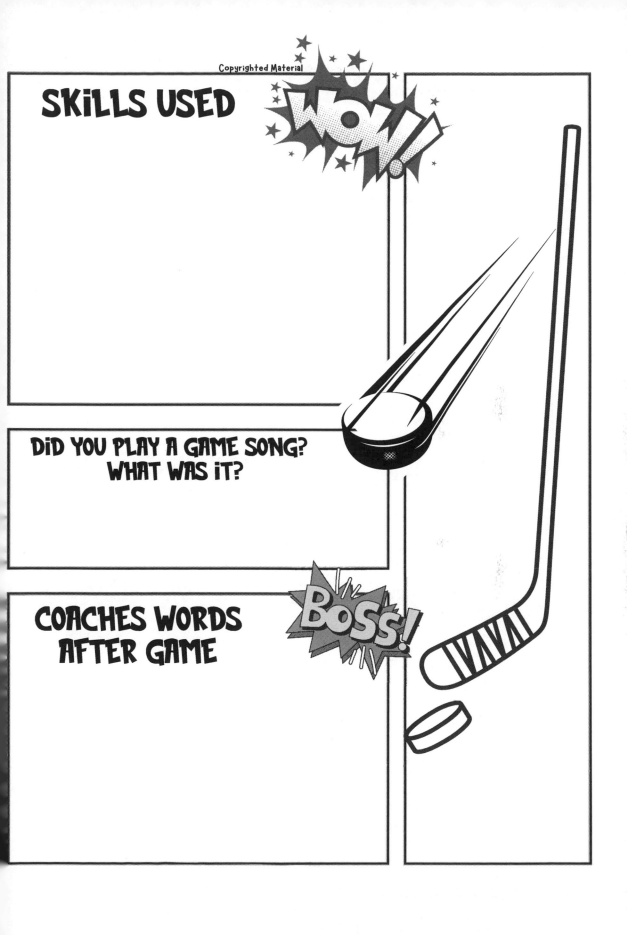

DID YOU PLAY A GAME SONG?
WHAT WAS IT?

COACHES WORDS
AFTER GAME

THINGS TO IMPROVE

WHAAA?!

FIGHTS?

KAPOW!

PENALTY MINUTES

BAD CALLS

ENHANCE THESE SKILLS

IT'S EASY TO THINK OF WINNING AS THE RESULT OF TALENT OR LUCK. REMEMBER THAT POSITIVE OUTCOMES ARE THE RESULT OF LOTS OF EFFORT. USUALLY THE BEST PLAYERS PRACTICE THE MOST AND WORK THE HARDEST!!

GAME DAY

DATE:

LOCATION:

START TIME: END TIME:

OPPONENT TEAM:

FROM:

OUTSIDE WEATHER

I WILL GIVE MY PERSONAL BEST AT ALL TIMES!

POW!

HAVE YOU PLAYED THIS TEAM BEFORE? RESULT:

DRAW THEIR JERSEY

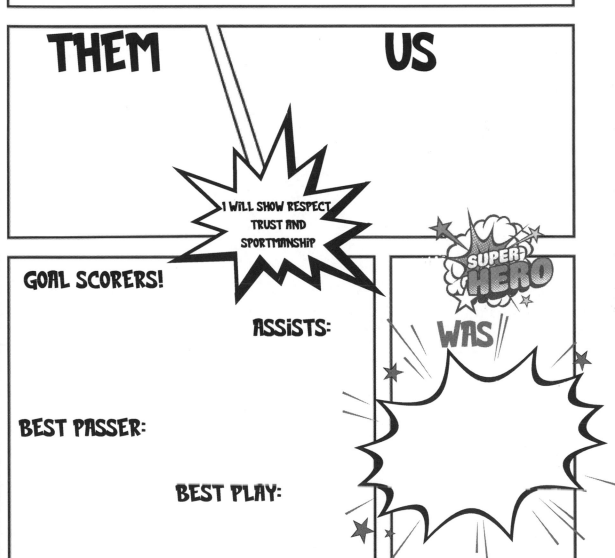

CiRCLE THE EMOJiS THAT BEST REPRESENT YOUR FEELiNGS AFTER THE GAME

OR DRAW YOUR OWN!

SKILLS USED

WOW!

DID YOU PLAY A GAME SONG? WHAT WAS IT?

COACHES WORDS AFTER GAME

BOSS!

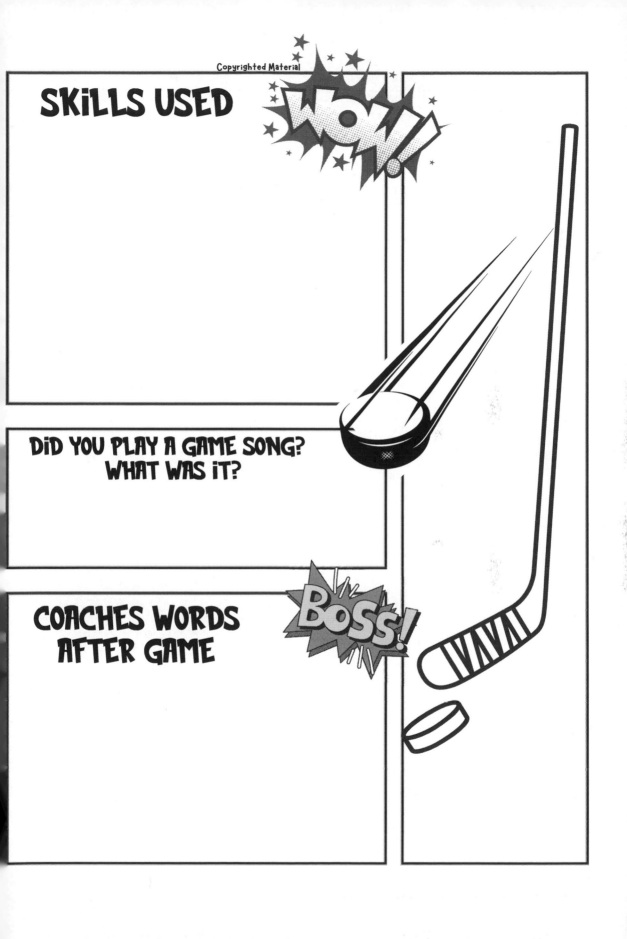

THINGS TO IMPROVE

WHAAAA?!

FIGHTS?

KAPOW!

PENALTY MINUTES

BAD CALLS

ENHANCE THESE SKILLS

DiD YOU RESPECT YOUR TEAMMATES?

DiD YOU PASS EFFECTIVELY?

DiD YOU CHEER FOR YOUR TEAM?

DiD YOU RESPECT YOUR OPPONENTS?

CHEER, NOT JEER!

DiD YOU PLAY BY THE RULES?

CONNECT WINNING WITH EFFORT!

DiD YOU SHAKE HANDS?

OTHER NOTES

IT'S EASY TO THINK OF WINNING AS THE RESULT OF TALENT OR LUCK. REMEMBER THAT POSITIVE OUTCOMES ARE THE RESULT OF LOTS OF EFFORT. USUALLY THE BEST PLAYERS PRACTICE THE MOST AND WORK THE HARDEST!!

GAME DAY

DATE:

LOCATION:

START TIME: **END TIME:**

OPPONENT TEAM:

FROM:

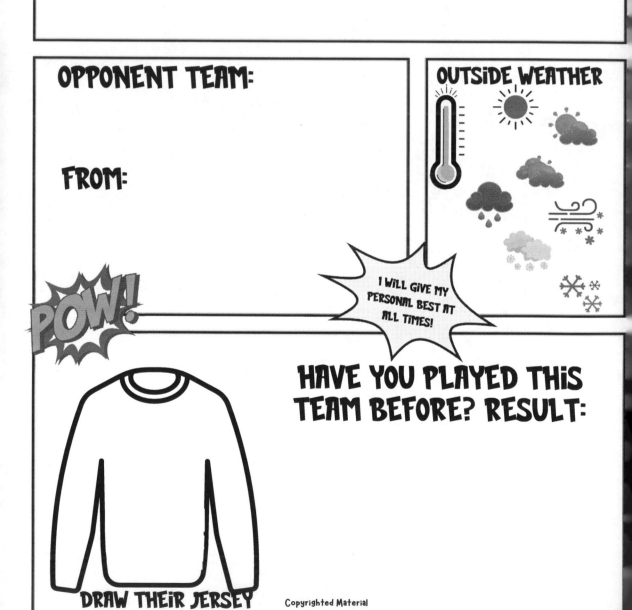

OUTSIDE WEATHER

I WILL GIVE MY PERSONAL BEST AT ALL TIMES!

POW!

HAVE YOU PLAYED THIS TEAM BEFORE? RESULT:

DRAW THEIR JERSEY

FINAL SCORE

THEM

US

I WILL SHOW RESPECT TRUST AND SPORTMANSHIP

WAS

GOAL SCORERS!

ASSISTS:

BEST PASSER:

BEST PLAY:

CIRCLE THE EMOJIS THAT BEST REPRESENT YOUR FEELINGS AFTER THE GAME

OR DRAW YOUR OWN!

SKILLS USED

DID YOU PLAY A GAME SONG? WHAT WAS IT?

COACHES WORDS AFTER GAME

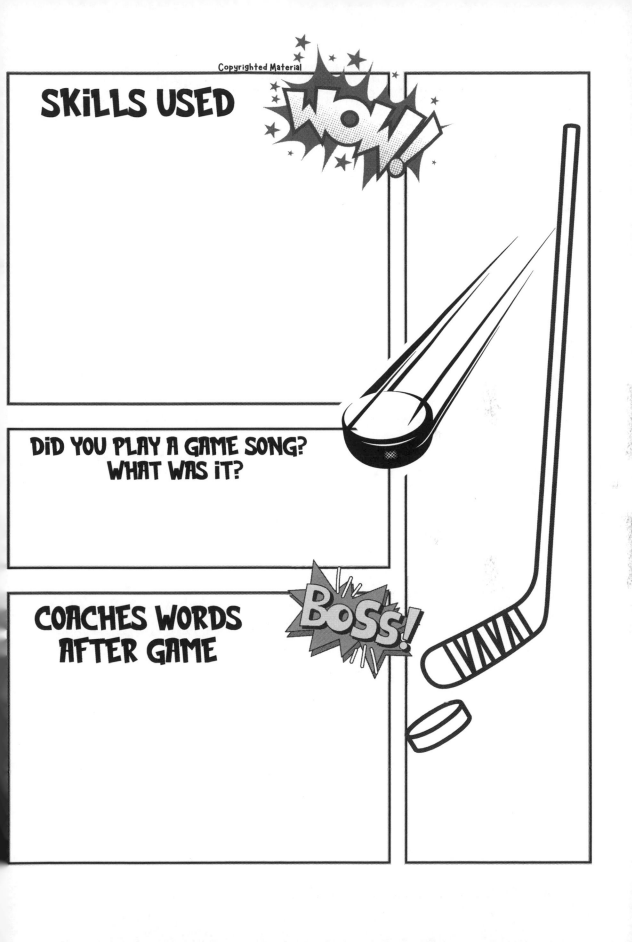

THINGS TO IMPROVE

WHAAA?!

F
I
G
H
T
S
?

KAPOW!

PENALTY MINUTES

BAD CALLS

ENHANCE THESE SKILLS

IT'S EASY TO THINK OF WINNING AS THE RESULT OF TALENT OR LUCK. REMEMBER THAT POSITIVE OUTCOMES ARE THE RESULT OF LOTS OF EFFORT. USUALLY THE BEST PLAYERS PRACTICE THE MOST AND WORK THE HARDEST!!

GAME DAY

DATE:

LOCATION:

START TIME: END TIME:

OPPONENT TEAM:

OUTSIDE WEATHER

FROM:

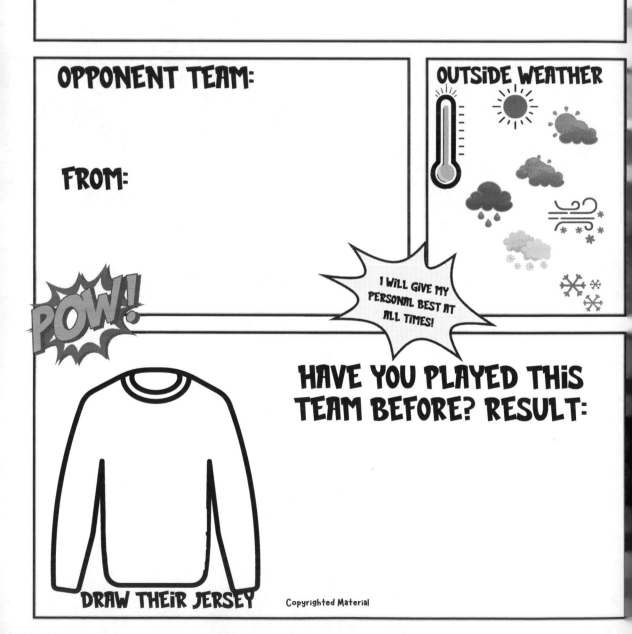

I WILL GIVE MY PERSONAL BEST AT ALL TIMES!

POW!

HAVE YOU PLAYED THIS TEAM BEFORE? RESULT:

DRAW THEIR JERSEY

FINAL SCORE

THEM

US

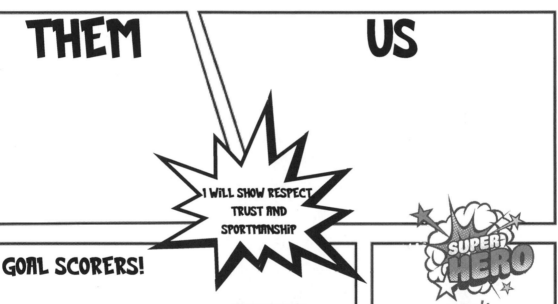

I WILL SHOW RESPECT TRUST AND SPORTMANSHIP

GOAL SCORERS!

ASSISTS:

BEST PASSER:

BEST PLAY:

SUPER HERO

WAS

CIRCLE THE EMOJIS THAT BEST REPRESENT YOUR FEELINGS AFTER THE GAME

OR DRAW YOUR OWN!

SKiLLS USED

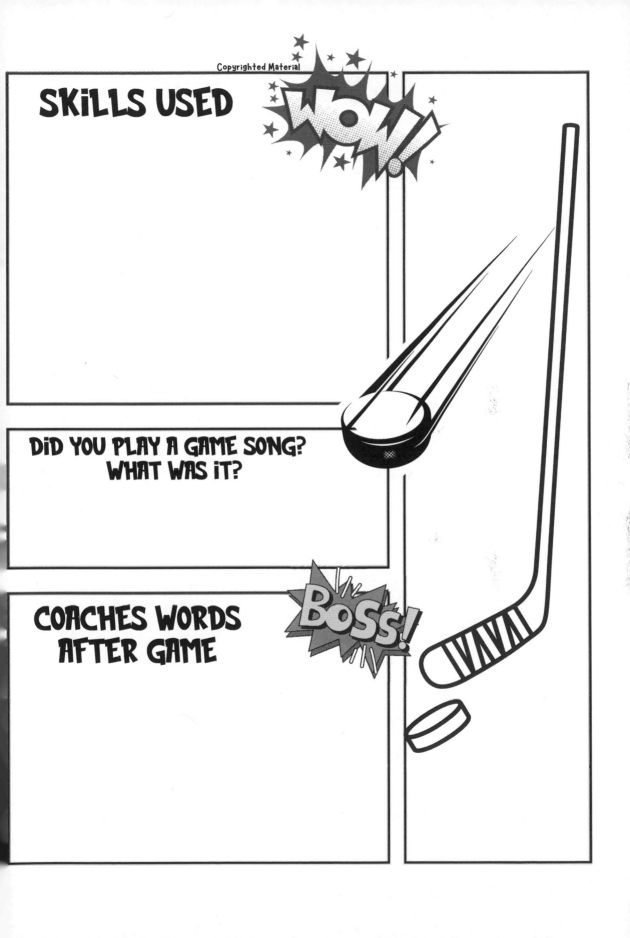

DiD YOU PLAY A GAME SONG? WHAT WAS iT?

COACHES WORDS AFTER GAME

THINGS TO IMPROVE

FiGHTS?

KAPOW!

WHAAAA?!

PENALTY MiNUTES

BAD CALLS

ENHANCE THESE SKILLS

DID YOU RESPECT YOUR TEAMMATES?

DID YOU PASS EFFECTIVELY?

DID YOU CHEER FOR YOUR TEAM?

DID YOU RESPECT YOUR OPPONENTS?

CHEER, NOT JEER!

DID YOU PLAY BY THE RULES?

CONNECT WINNING WITH EFFORT!

DID YOU SHAKE HANDS?

OTHER NOTES

IT'S EASY TO THINK OF WINNING AS THE RESULT OF TALENT OR LUCK. REMEMBER THAT POSITIVE OUTCOMES ARE THE RESULT OF LOTS OF EFFORT. USUALLY THE BEST PLAYERS PRACTICE THE MOST AND WORK THE HARDEST!!

GAME DAY

DATE:

LOCATION:

START TIME: **END TIME:**

OPPONENT TEAM:

FROM:

OUTSIDE WEATHER

I WILL GIVE MY PERSONAL BEST AT ALL TIMES!

POW!

HAVE YOU PLAYED THIS TEAM BEFORE? RESULT:

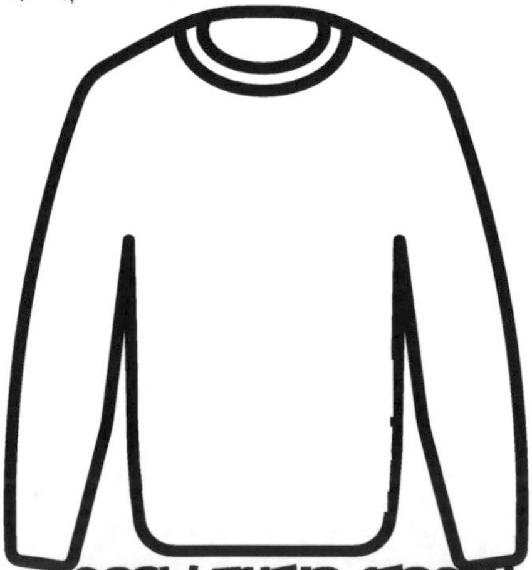

DRAW THEIR JERSEY

FINAL SCORE

THEM

US

I WILL SHOW RESPECT TRUST AND SPORTMANSHIP

SUPER HERO

WAS

GOAL SCORERS!

ASSISTS:

BEST PASSER:

BEST PLAY:

CIRCLE THE EMOJIS THAT BEST REPRESENT YOUR FEELINGS AFTER THE GAME

OR DRAW YOUR OWN!

SKILLS USED

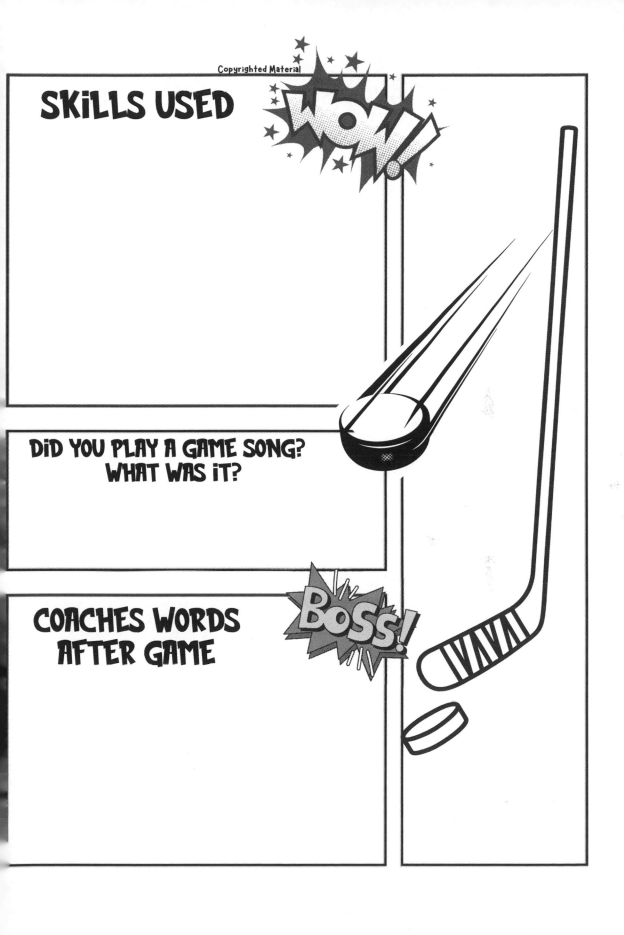

DID YOU PLAY A GAME SONG? WHAT WAS IT?

COACHES WORDS AFTER GAME

THINGS TO IMPROVE

WHAAAA?!

FIGHTS?

KAPOW!!

PENALTY MINUTES

BAD CALLS

ENHANCE THESE SKILLS

DID YOU RESPECT YOUR TEAMMATES?

DID YOU PASS EFFECTIVELY?

DID YOU CHEER FOR YOUR TEAM?

DID YOU RESPECT YOUR OPPONENTS?

CHEER, NOT JEER!

DID YOU PLAY BY THE RULES?

CONNECT WINNING WITH EFFORT!

DID YOU SHAKE HANDS?

OTHER NOTES

IT'S EASY TO THINK OF WINNING AS THE RESULT OF TALENT OR LUCK. REMEMBER THAT POSITIVE OUTCOMES ARE THE RESULT OF LOTS OF EFFORT. USUALLY THE BEST PLAYERS PRACTICE THE MOST AND WORK THE HARDEST!!

GAME DAY

DATE:

LOCATION:

START TIME: END TIME:

OPPONENT TEAM:

FROM:

OUTSIDE WEATHER

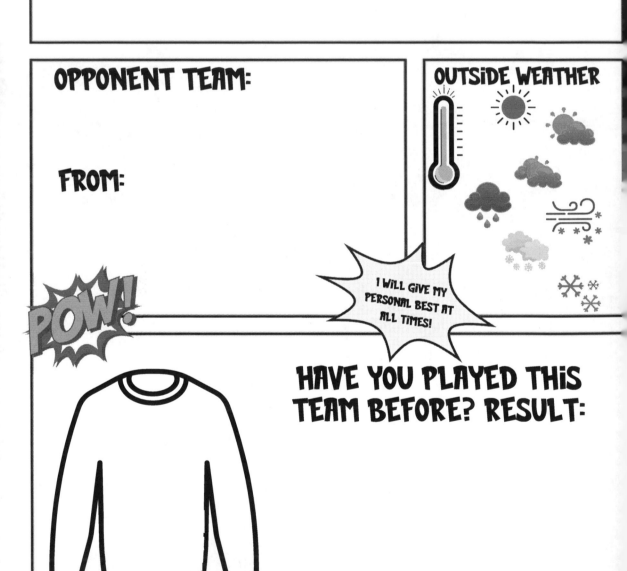

I WILL GIVE MY PERSONAL BEST AT ALL TIMES!

POW!

HAVE YOU PLAYED THIS TEAM BEFORE? RESULT:

DRAW THEIR JERSEY

FINAL SCORE

THEM   US

I WILL SHOW RESPECT TRUST AND SPORTMANSHIP

GOAL SCORERS!

ASSISTS:

SUPER HERO WAS

BEST PASSER:

BEST PLAY:

CIRCLE THE EMOJIS THAT BEST REPRESENT YOUR FEELINGS AFTER THE GAME

OR DRAW YOUR OWN!

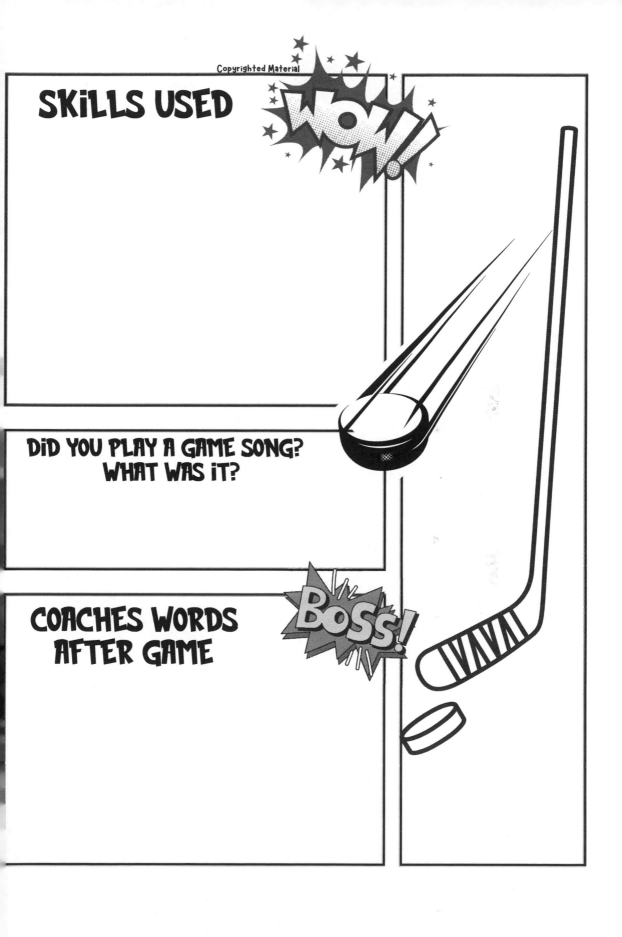

SKILLS USED

WOW!

DID YOU PLAY A GAME SONG? WHAT WAS IT?

COACHES WORDS AFTER GAME

BOSS!

THiNGS TO IMPROVE

WHAAA?!

FiGHTS?

KAPOW!

PENALTY MiNUTES

BAD CALLS

ENHANCE THESE SKILLS

DiD YOU RESPECT YOUR TEAMMATES?

DiD YOU PASS EFFECTIVELY?

DiD YOU CHEER FOR YOUR TEAM?

DiD YOU RESPECT YOUR OPPONENTS?

CHEER, NOT JEER!

DiD YOU PLAY BY THE RULES?

CONNECT WINNING WITH EFFORT!

DiD YOU SHAKE HANDS?

OTHER NOTES

IT'S EASY TO THINK OF WINNING AS THE RESULT OF TALENT OR LUCK. REMEMBER THAT POSITIVE OUTCOMES ARE THE RESULT OF LOTS OF EFFORT. USUALLY THE BEST PLAYERS PRACTICE THE MOST AND WORK THE HARDEST!!

GAME DAY

DATE:

LOCATION:

START TIME: END TIME:

OPPONENT TEAM:

FROM:

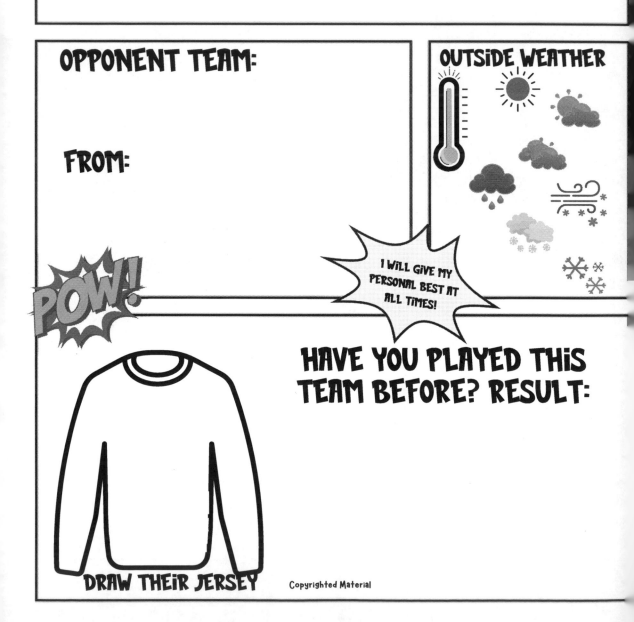

OUTSIDE WEATHER

I WILL GIVE MY PERSONAL BEST AT ALL TIMES!

POW!!

HAVE YOU PLAYED THIS TEAM BEFORE? RESULT:

DRAW THEIR JERSEY

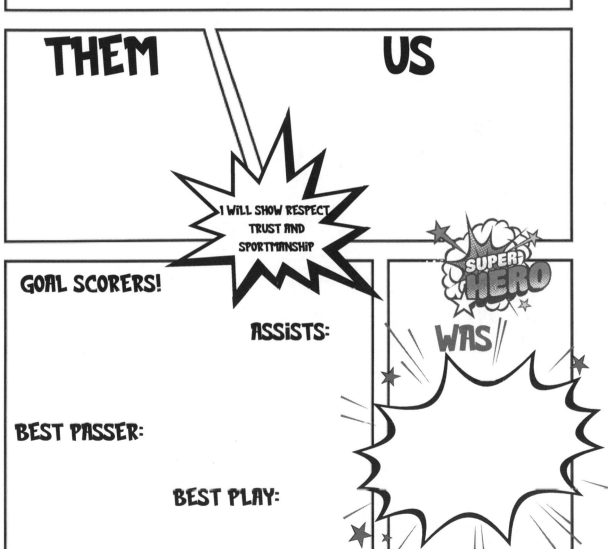

CIRCLE THE EMOJIS THAT BEST REPRESENT YOUR FEELINGS AFTER THE GAME

OR DRAW YOUR OWN!

SKILLS USED

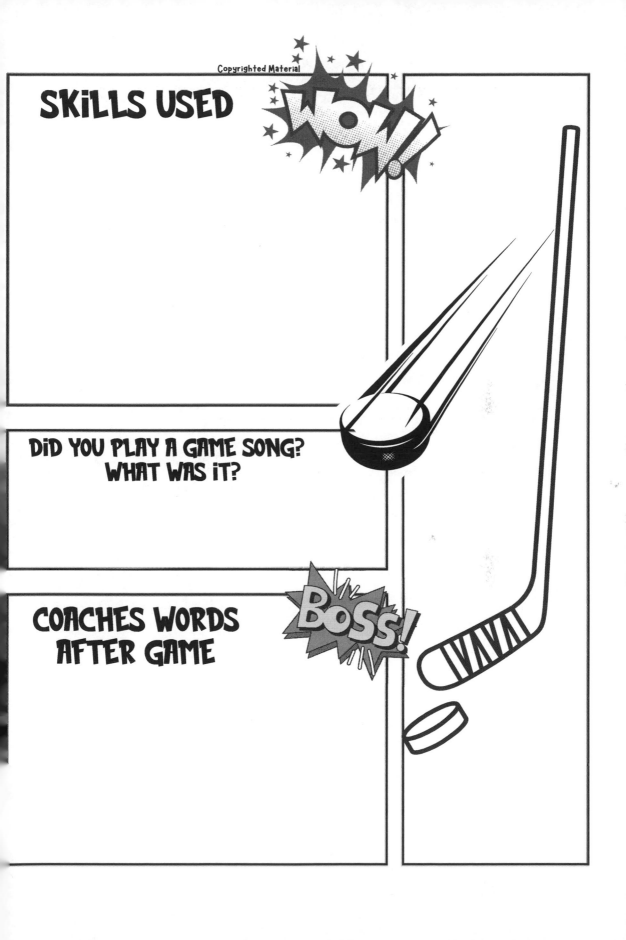

DID YOU PLAY A GAME SONG? WHAT WAS IT?

COACHES WORDS AFTER GAME

THINGS TO IMPROVE

WHAAA?!

FIGHTS?

KAPOW!

PENALTY MINUTES

BAD CALLS

ENHANCE THESE SKILLS

DiD YOU RESPECT YOUR TEAMMATES?

DiD YOU PASS EFFECTIVELY?

DiD YOU CHEER FOR YOUR TEAM?

DiD YOU RESPECT YOUR OPPONENTS?

CHEER, NOT JEER!

DiD YOU PLAY BY THE RULES?

CONNECT WINNING WITH EFFORT!

DiD YOU SHAKE HANDS?

OTHER NOTES

IT'S EASY TO THINK OF WINNING AS THE RESULT OF TALENT OR LUCK. REMEMBER THAT POSITIVE OUTCOMES ARE THE RESULT OF LOTS OF EFFORT. USUALLY THE BEST PLAYERS PRACTICE THE MOST AND WORK THE HARDEST!!

GAME DAY

DATE:

LOCATION:

START TIME: END TIME:

OPPONENT TEAM:

FROM:

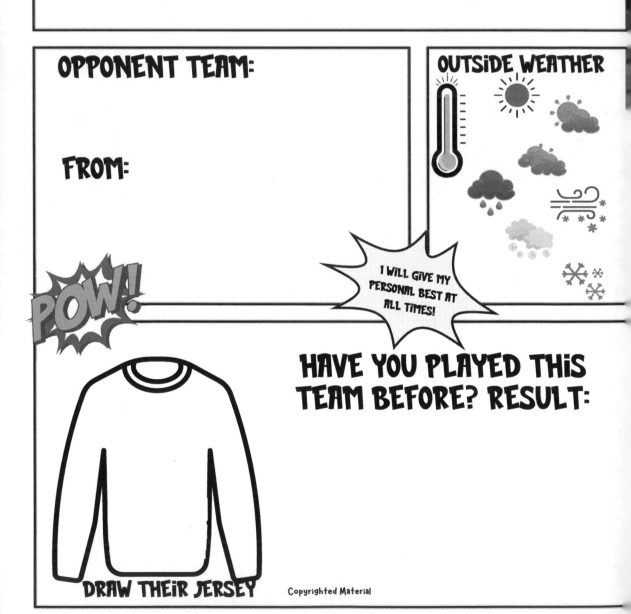

OUTSIDE WEATHER

I WILL GIVE MY PERSONAL BEST AT ALL TIMES!

POW!

HAVE YOU PLAYED THIS TEAM BEFORE? RESULT:

DRAW THEIR JERSEY

FINAL SCORE

  **LOSS**

THEM

US

I WILL SHOW RESPECT TRUST AND SPORTMANSHIP

GOAL SCORERS!

ASSISTS:

WAS

BEST PASSER:

BEST PLAY:

CIRCLE THE EMOJIS THAT BEST REPRESENT YOUR FEELINGS AFTER THE GAME

OR DRAW YOUR OWN!

SKILLS USED

DID YOU PLAY A GAME SONG? WHAT WAS IT?

COACHES WORDS AFTER GAME

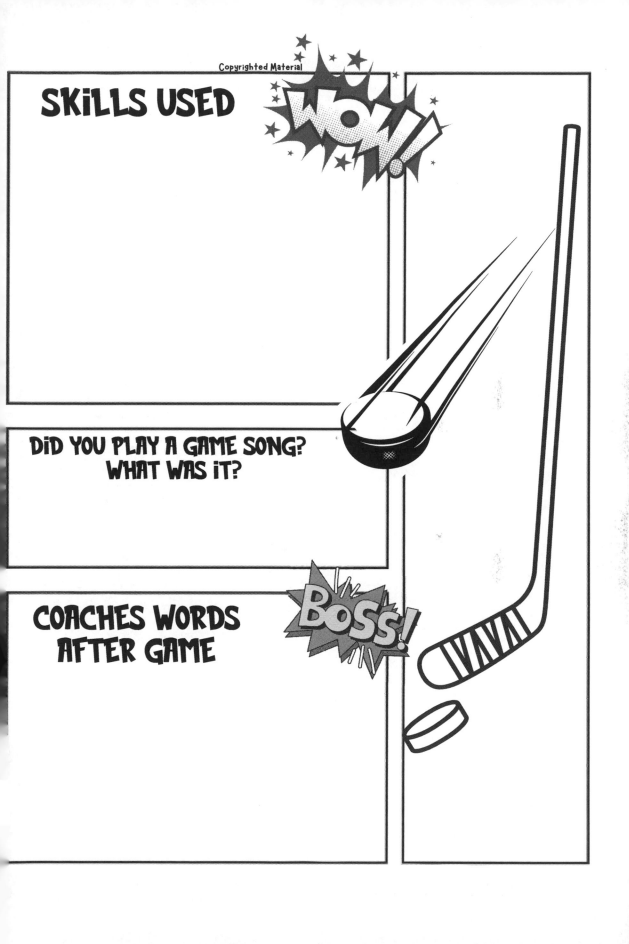

THINGS TO IMPROVE

WHAAAA?!

FIGHTS?

KAPOW!

PENALTY MINUTES

BAD CALLS

ENHANCE THESE SKILLS

!

DiD YOU RESPECT YOUR TEAMMATES?

DiD YOU PASS EFFECTIVELY?

DiD YOU CHEER FOR YOUR TEAM?

DiD YOU RESPECT YOUR OPPONENTS?

CHEER, NOT JEER!

DiD YOU PLAY BY THE RULES?

CONNECT WINNING WITH EFFORT!

DiD YOU SHAKE HANDS?

OTHER NOTES

IT'S EASY TO THINK OF WINNING AS THE RESULT OF TALENT OR LUCK. REMEMBER THAT POSITIVE OUTCOMES ARE THE RESULT OF LOTS OF EFFORT. USUALLY THE BEST PLAYERS PRACTICE THE MOST AND WORK THE HARDEST!!

GAME DAY

DATE:

LOCATION:

START TIME: **END TIME:**

OPPONENT TEAM:

FROM:

OUTSIDE WEATHER

I WILL GIVE MY PERSONAL BEST AT ALL TIMES!

POW!

HAVE YOU PLAYED THIS TEAM BEFORE? RESULT:

DRAW THEIR JERSEY

FINAL SCORE

THEM

US

I WILL SHOW RESPECT TRUST AND SPORTMANSHIP

SUPER! HERO WAS

GOAL SCORERS!

ASSISTS:

BEST PASSER:

BEST PLAY:

CiRCLE THE EMOJiS THAT BEST REPRESENT YOUR FEELINGS AFTER THE GAME

OR DRAW YOUR OWN!

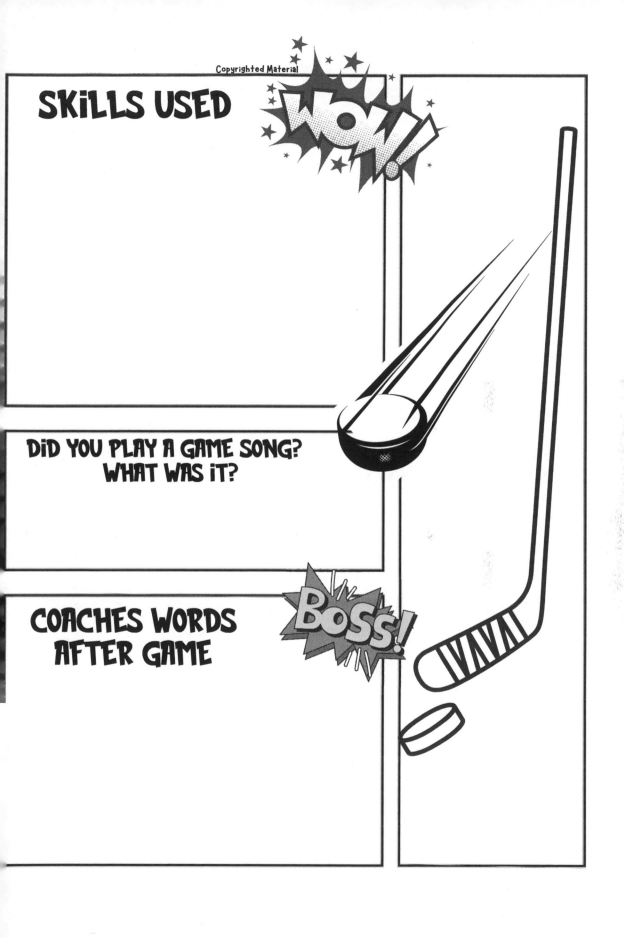

SKILLS USED

DID YOU PLAY A GAME SONG? WHAT WAS IT?

COACHES WORDS AFTER GAME

THINGS TO IMPROVE

WHAAAA?!

FIGHTS?

KAPOW!

PENALTY MINUTES

BAD CALLS

ENHANCE THESE SKILLS

DID YOU RESPECT YOUR TEAMMATES?

DID YOU PASS EFFECTIVELY?

DID YOU CHEER FOR YOUR TEAM?

DID YOU RESPECT YOUR OPPONENTS?

CHEER, NOT JEER!

DID YOU PLAY BY THE RULES?

CONNECT WINNING WITH EFFORT!

DID YOU SHAKE HANDS?

OTHER NOTES

IT'S EASY TO THINK OF WINNING AS THE RESULT OF TALENT OR LUCK. REMEMBER THAT POSITIVE OUTCOMES ARE THE RESULT OF LOTS OF EFFORT. USUALLY THE BEST PLAYERS PRACTICE THE MOST AND WORK THE HARDEST!!

GAME DAY

DATE:

LOCATION:

START TIME: END TIME:

OPPONENT TEAM:

FROM:

OUTSIDE WEATHER

I WILL GIVE MY PERSONAL BEST AT ALL TIMES!

POW!!

HAVE YOU PLAYED THIS TEAM BEFORE? RESULT:

DRAW THEIR JERSEY

FINAL SCORE

WIN! OUCH! YEAH!! LOSS

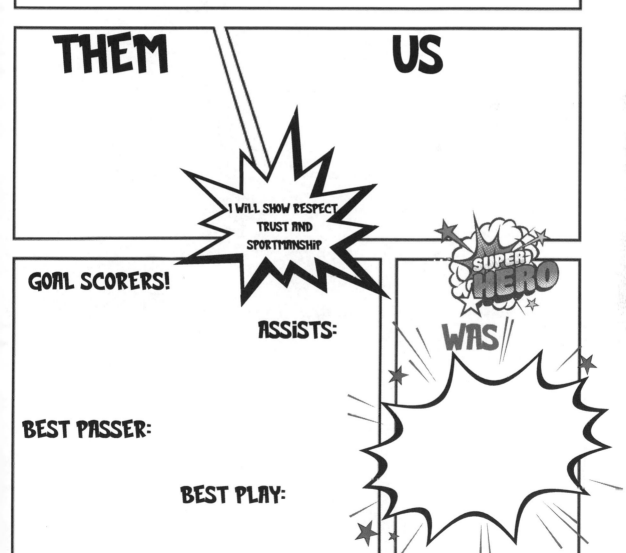

THEM

US

I WILL SHOW RESPECT TRUST AND SPORTMANSHIP

GOAL SCORERS!

ASSISTS:

SUPER HERO WAS

BEST PASSER:

BEST PLAY:

CIRCLE THE EMOJIS THAT BEST REPRESENT YOUR FEELINGS AFTER THE GAME

OR DRAW YOUR OWN!

SKILLS USED

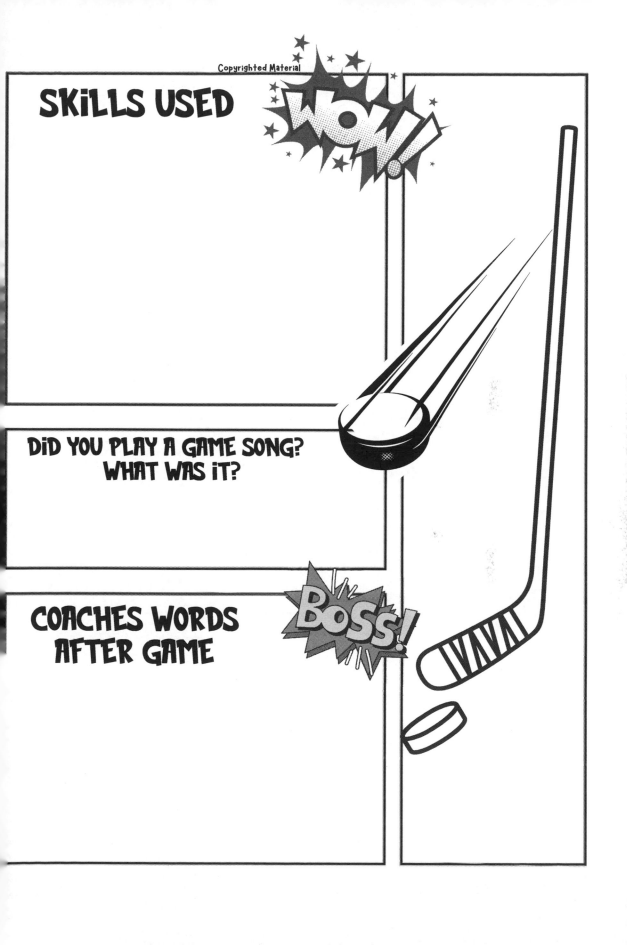

DID YOU PLAY A GAME SONG? WHAT WAS IT?

COACHES WORDS AFTER GAME

THINGS TO IMPROVE

WHAAAA?!

FIGHTS?

KAPOW!

PENALTY MINUTES

BAD CALLS

ENHANCE THESE SKILLS

DID YOU RESPECT YOUR TEAMMATES?

DID YOU PASS EFFECTIVELY?

DID YOU CHEER FOR YOUR TEAM?

DID YOU RESPECT YOUR OPPONENTS?

CHEER, NOT JEER!

DID YOU PLAY BY THE RULES?

CONNECT WINNING WITH EFFORT!

DID YOU SHAKE HANDS?

OTHER NOTES

IT'S EASY TO THINK OF WINNING AS THE RESULT OF TALENT OR LUCK. REMEMBER THAT POSITIVE OUTCOMES ARE THE RESULT OF LOTS OF EFFORT. USUALLY THE BEST PLAYERS PRACTICE THE MOST AND WORK THE HARDEST!!

GAME DAY

DATE:

LOCATION:

START TIME: **END TIME:**

OPPONENT TEAM:

FROM:

OUTSIDE WEATHER

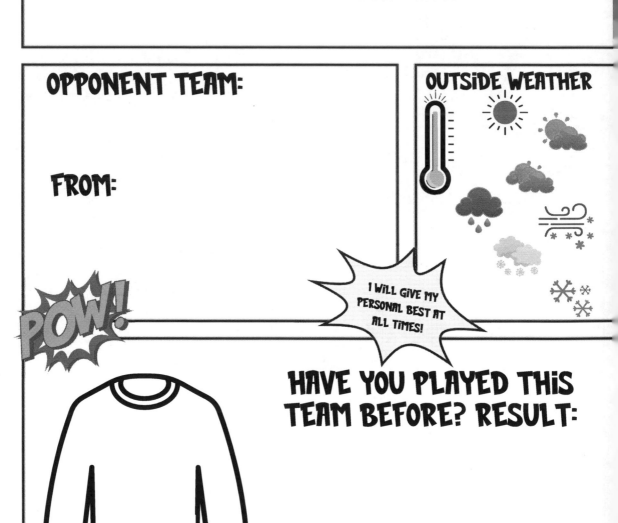

I WILL GIVE MY PERSONAL BEST AT ALL TIMES!

POW!

HAVE YOU PLAYED THIS TEAM BEFORE? RESULT:

DRAW THEIR JERSEY

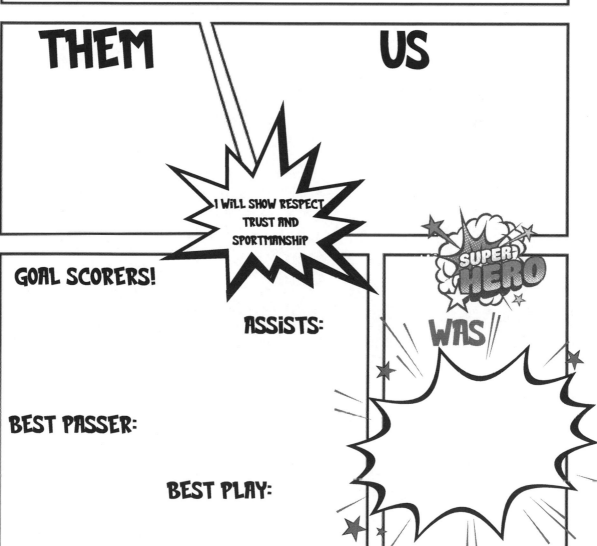

CIRCLE THE EMOJIS THAT BEST REPRESENT YOUR FEELINGS AFTER THE GAME

OR DRAW YOUR OWN!

SKILLS USED

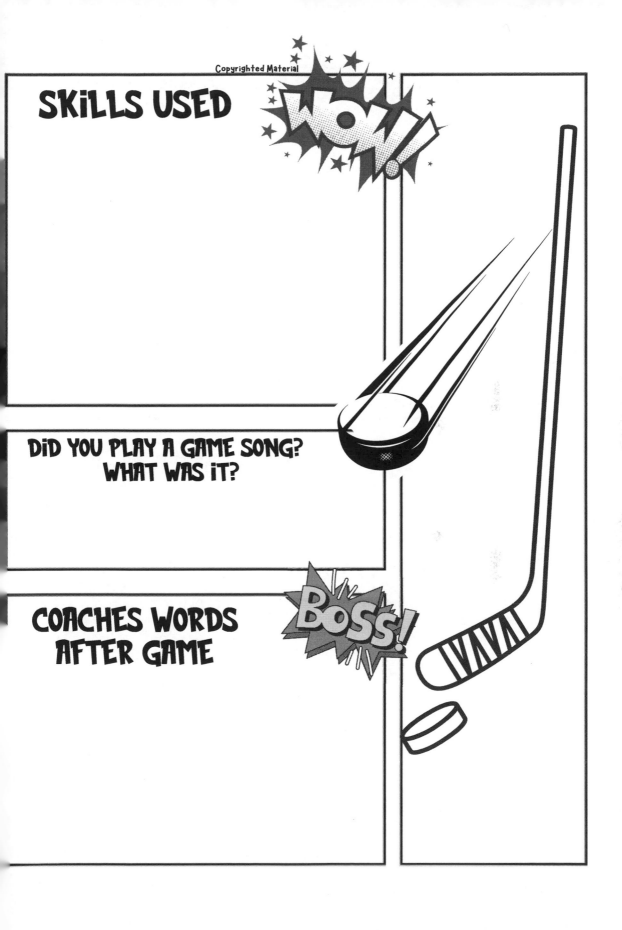

DID YOU PLAY A GAME SONG? WHAT WAS IT?

COACHES WORDS AFTER GAME

THINGS TO IMPROVE

WHAAA?!

FIGHTS?

KAPOW!

PENALTY MINUTES

BAD CALLS

ENHANCE THESE SKILLS

DID YOU RESPECT YOUR TEAMMATES?

DID YOU PASS EFFECTIVELY?

DID YOU CHEER FOR YOUR TEAM?

DID YOU RESPECT YOUR OPPONENTS?

CHEER, NOT JEER!

DID YOU PLAY BY THE RULES?

CONNECT WINNING WITH EFFORT!

DID YOU SHAKE HANDS?

OTHER NOTES

IT'S EASY TO THINK OF WINNING AS THE RESULT OF TALENT OR LUCK. REMEMBER THAT POSITIVE OUTCOMES ARE THE RESULT OF LOTS OF EFFORT. USUALLY THE BEST PLAYERS PRACTICE THE MOST AND WORK THE HARDEST!!

GAME DAY

DATE:

LOCATION:

START TIME: **END TIME:**

OPPONENT TEAM:

FROM:

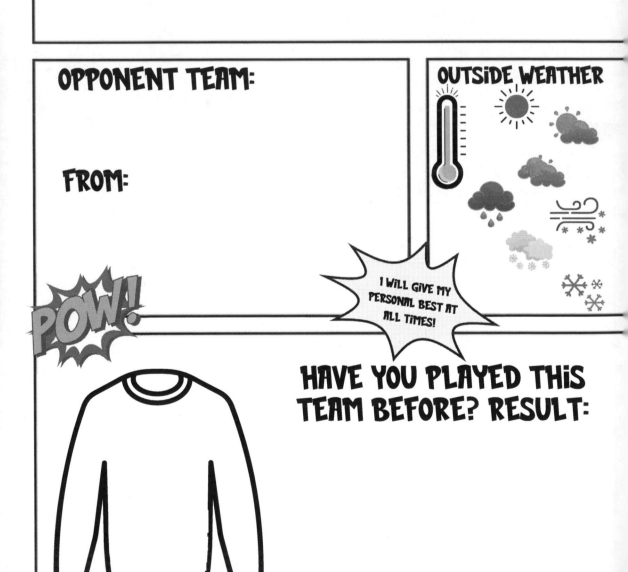

OUTSIDE WEATHER

I WILL GIVE MY PERSONAL BEST AT ALL TIMES!

POW!

HAVE YOU PLAYED THIS TEAM BEFORE? RESULT:

DRAW THEIR JERSEY

FINAL SCORE

THEM

US

I WILL SHOW RESPECT TRUST AND SPORTMANSHIP

GOAL SCORERS!

ASSISTS:

SUPER HERO WAS

BEST PASSER:

BEST PLAY:

CIRCLE THE EMOJIS THAT BEST REPRESENT YOUR FEELINGS AFTER THE GAME

OR DRAW YOUR OWN!

SKILLS USED

DID YOU PLAY A GAME SONG? WHAT WAS IT?

COACHES WORDS AFTER GAME

THINGS TO IMPROVE

WHAAAA?!

FIGHTS?

KAPOW!

PENALTY MINUTES

BAD CALLS

ENHANCE THESE SKILLS

DiD YOU RESPECT YOUR TEAMMATES?

DiD YOU PASS EFFECTIVELY?

DiD YOU CHEER FOR YOUR TEAM?

DiD YOU RESPECT YOUR OPPONENTS?

CHEER, NOT JEER!

DiD YOU PLAY BY THE RULES?

CONNECT WINNING WITH EFFORT!

DiD YOU SHAKE HANDS?

OTHER NOTES

IT'S EASY TO THINK OF WINNING AS THE RESULT OT TALENT OR LUCK. REMEMBER THAT POSITIVE OUTCOMES ARE THE RESULT OF LOTS OF EFFORT. USUALLY THE BEST PLAYERS PRACTICE THE MOST AND WORK THE HARDEST!!

GAME DAY

DATE:

LOCATION:

START TIME: **END TIME:**

OPPONENT TEAM:

FROM:

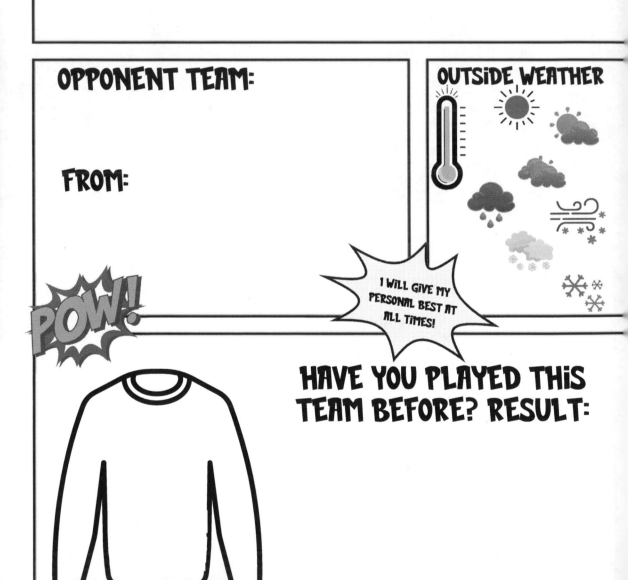

OUTSIDE WEATHER

I WILL GIVE MY PERSONAL BEST AT ALL TIMES!

POW!

HAVE YOU PLAYED THIS TEAM BEFORE? RESULT:

DRAW THEIR JERSEY

FINAL SCORE

WIN! OUCH! YEAH!! LOSS

THEM

US

I WILL SHOW RESPECT TRUST AND SPORTMANSHIP

SUPER HERO WAS

GOAL SCORERS!

ASSISTS:

BEST PASSER:

BEST PLAY:

CIRCLE THE EMOJIS THAT BEST REPRESENT YOUR FEELINGS AFTER THE GAME

OR DRAW YOUR OWN!

SKiLLS USED

DiD YOU PLAY A GAME SONG?
WHAT WAS iT?

COACHES WORDS
AFTER GAME

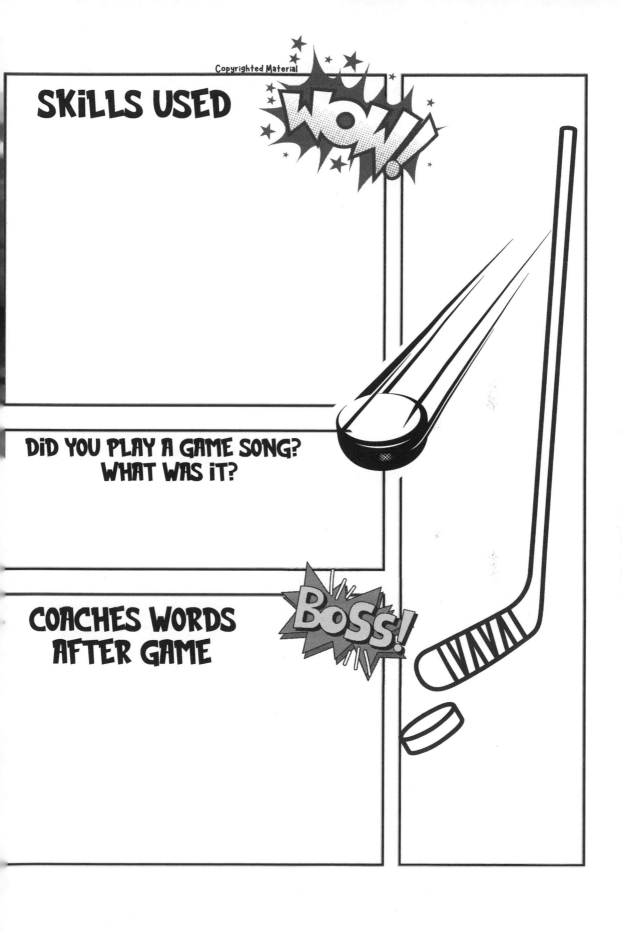

THINGS TO IMPROVE

WHAAAA?!

F I G H T S ?

KAPOW!

PENALTY MINUTES

BAD CALLS

ENHANCE THESE SKILLS

DID YOU RESPECT YOUR TEAMMATES?

DID YOU PASS EFFECTIVELY?

DID YOU CHEER FOR YOUR TEAM?

DID YOU RESPECT YOUR OPPONENTS?

CHEER, NOT JEER!

DID YOU PLAY BY THE RULES?

CONNECT WINNING WITH EFFORT!

DID YOU SHAKE HANDS?

OTHER NOTES

IT'S EASY TO THINK OF WINNING AS THE RESULT OF TALENT OR LUCK. REMEMBER THAT POSITIVE OUTCOMES ARE THE RESULT OF LOTS OF EFFORT. USUALLY THE BEST PLAYERS PRACTICE THE MOST AND WORK THE HARDEST!!

GAME DAY

DATE:

LOCATION:

START TIME: **END TIME:**

OPPONENT TEAM:

FROM:

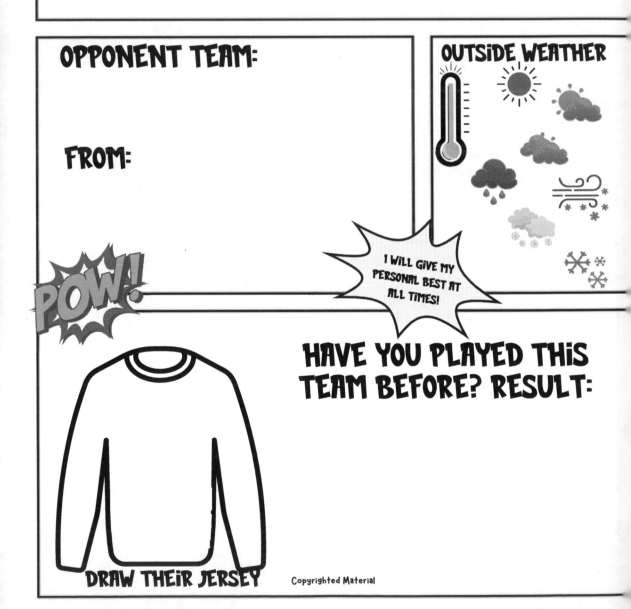

OUTSIDE WEATHER

I WILL GIVE MY PERSONAL BEST AT ALL TIMES!

POW!

HAVE YOU PLAYED THIS TEAM BEFORE? RESULT:

DRAW THEIR JERSEY

FINAL SCORE

WIN! OUGH! YEAH!! LOSS

THEM

US

I WILL SHOW RESPECT TRUST AND SPORTMANSHIP

GOAL SCORERS!

ASSISTS:

SUPER HERO WAS

BEST PASSER:

BEST PLAY:

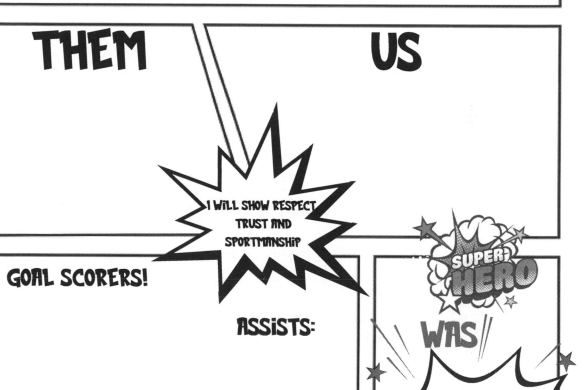

CIRCLE THE EMOJiS THAT BEST REPRESENT YOUR FEELiNGS AFTER THE GAME

OR DRAW YOUR OWN!

SKILLS USED

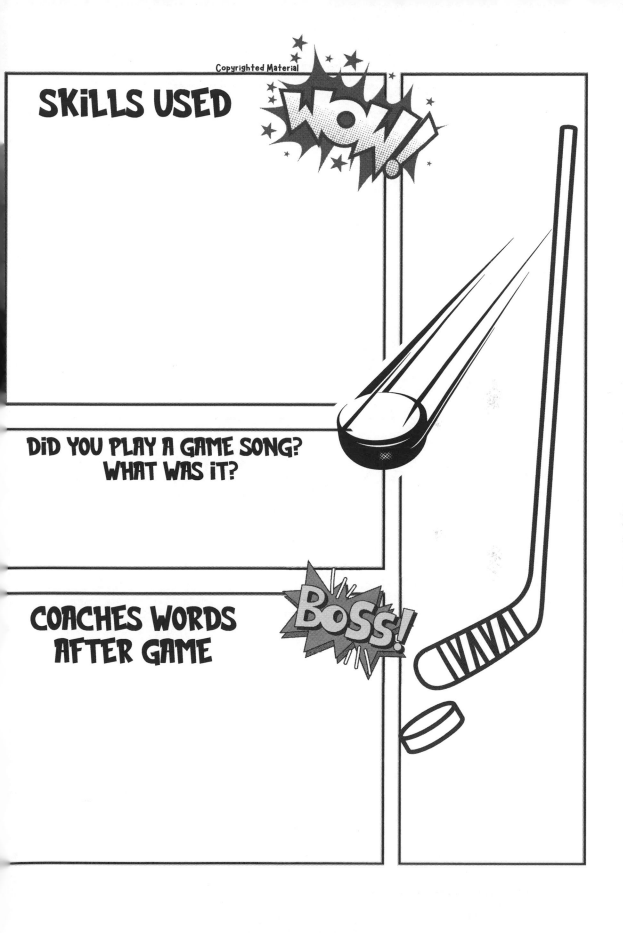

DID YOU PLAY A GAME SONG? WHAT WAS IT?

COACHES WORDS AFTER GAME

THINGS TO IMPROVE

WHAAAA?!

FIGHTS?

KAPOW!

PENALTY MINUTES

BAD CALLS

ENHANCE THESE SKILLS

DiD YOU RESPECT YOUR TEAMMATES?

DiD YOU PASS EFFECTIVELY?

DiD YOU CHEER FOR YOUR TEAM?

DiD YOU RESPECT YOUR OPPONENTS?

CHEER, NOT JEER!

DiD YOU PLAY BY THE RULES?

CONNECT WINNING WITH EFFORT!

DiD YOU SHAKE HANDS?

OTHER NOTES

IT'S EASY TO THINK OF WINNING AS THE RESULT OF TALENT OR LUCK. REMEMBER THAT POSITIVE OUTCOMES ARE THE RESULT OF LOTS OF EFFORT. USUALLY THE BEST PLAYERS PRACTICE THE MOST AND WORK THE HARDEST!!

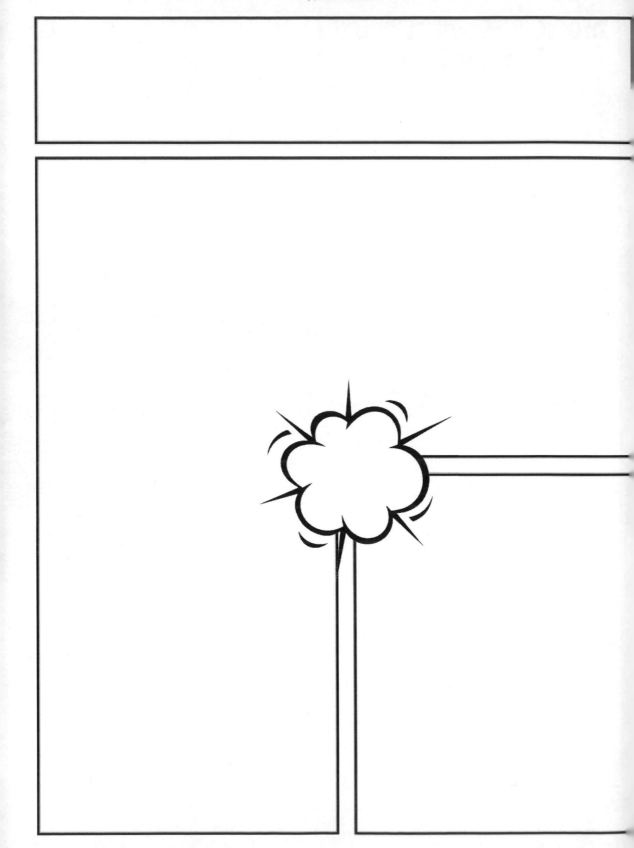

END OF SEASON

END OF SEASON SUMMARY

STATS!

PLAYERS, COACHES AND PARENTS KNOW WHEN PLAYERS ARE PERFORMING WELL AND DO NOT NEED TO SEE NUMBERS TO PROVE IT.

THAT BEING SAID, MOST KIDS WANT TO KNOW HOW THEY ARE PERFORMING AND FOR EACH CHILD THESE STATISTICS ARE DIFFERENT. ONE CHILD MAY CARE MORE ABOUT HOW MANY GOALS THEY GOT VERSES SOMEONE WHO WANTS TO KNOW HOW MANY SHOTS THEY ATTEMPTED. THIS AREA THEREFORE, IS INTENTIONALLY LEFT FREE FORM FOR YOU TO HIGHLIGHT THE STATISTICS THAT ARE IMPORTANT TO YOU. FEEL FREE TO LIST ALL THE STATISTICS YOU WANT TO REMEMBER FOR NEXT YEAR AND FOR YEARS TO COME.

JUST REMEMBER, THIS IS A TEAM GAME AND INDIVIDUAL STATISTICS CAN GET IN THE WAY OF THE TEAM. MAKE SURE YOU DON'T PLAY JUST FOR STATISTICS, INSTEAD OF FOCUSING ON WINNING GAMES AND BEING TEAM PLAYERS. CONFIDENCE COMES WHEN PLAYERS KNOW THEY ARE TRENDING IN THE RIGHT DIRECTION.

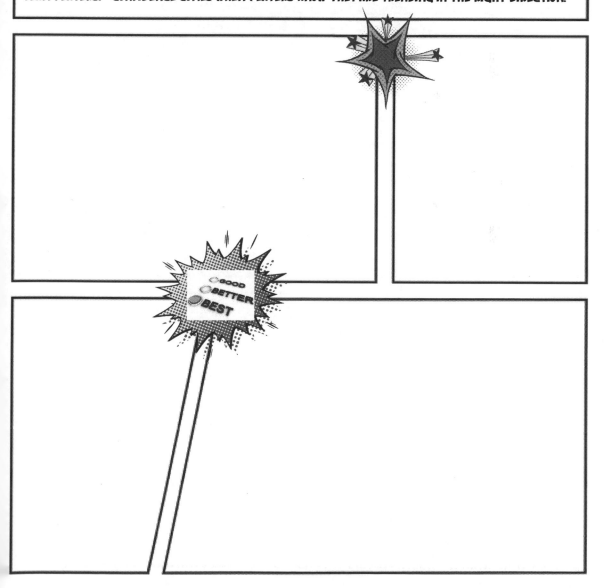

END OF SEASON SUMMARY

WHAT ARE MY GOALS FOR NEXT SEASON?

WHAT I NEED TO IMPROVE

BEST FRIENDS ON TEAM

You Win!

Made in the USA
Las Vegas, NV
24 September 2022

55895671R00098